INVENTION AND
THE EVOLUTION OF IDEAS

An examination of the emergence of novelty
—in theories and in scientific discovery and
invention—leads the author to postulate a
unifying principle, *the displacement of concepts*, in terms of which a variety of phenomena may be seen as manifestations of a
single underlying process. In exploring the
scope of this principle, which he discusses
in relation to metaphor, analogy, and comparison, Dr Schon draws examples from
concrete cases of product development and
invention in industry; from the history of
science; from theories in philosophy, aesthetics, and the human sciences; from the
forms of language; and from common-
sense beliefs.

'It would not be an exaggeration to say that
Schon's argument puts new interpretations
on the history of ideas.' B. M. Foss, *British
Journal of Aesthetics*

'This stimulating and original book.' Mary
Hesse, *New Scientist*

'It is a lively book, well illustrated by examples both from the history of ideas and
from current technical invention.' L. S.
Hearnshaw, *British Journal of Psychology*

SOCIAL SCIENCE PAPERBACKS
SSP 13

FORMERLY PUBLISHED AS

Displacement of Concepts

Invention and
the Evolution of Ideas

DONALD A. SCHON

SOCIAL SCIENCE PAPERBACKS

in association with

TAVISTOCK PUBLICATIONS

First published in 1963
as 'Displacement of Concepts'
by Tavistock Publications Ltd
11 New Fetter Lane London EC4
First published in this series 1967
© 1963 by Donald A. Schon
Printed and bound in Great Britain
by Butler & Tanner Ltd, Frome and London

SOCIAL SCIENCE PAPERBACKS
are published by members of
Associated Book Publishers Ltd
11 New Fetter Lane London EC4

CONTENTS

Contents

ACKNOWLEDGEMENTS

Thanks are due to the individuals and publishers concerned for permission to quote passages from the following works:

The Cambridge University Press in respect of *Patterns of Discovery* by Norwood Russell Hanson; The Clarendon Press, Oxford, in respect of *The Allegory of Love* by C. S. Lewis; The Estate of Albert Einstein in respect of *The Evolution of Physics* by Albert Einstein and Leopold Infeld; Faber & Faber in respect of *Passion and Society* by Denis de Rougemont (published in the U.S.A. by Pantheon Books under the title *Love in the Western World*); Harper and Row in respect of *Productive Thinking* by Max Wertheimer, *Language and Myth* by Ernst Cassirer; The Harvard University Press in respect of *Philosophy in a New Key* by Susanne K. Langer; Holt, Rinehart and Winston, Inc., in respect of *The Forgotten Language* by Erich Fromm; The Houghton Mifflin Company in respect of *Epaminondas and His Auntie* by Sarah Cone Bryant; Hutchinson & Company in respect of *The Philosophy of Science* by Stephen Toulmin; J. Vrin in respect of *Le Concept d'analogie* by Harald Hoffding; The Macmillan Company in respect of *Shorter History of Science* by William Cecil Dampier, *Words and Things* by Roger Brown; The McGraw-Hill Book Company, Inc., in respect of *Dynamic Theory of Personality* by Kurt Lewin (Copyright 1935); New American Library of World Literature in respect of *The Notebooks of Leonardo da Vinci, A New Selection* by Pamela Taylor; W. W. Norton & Co., Inc., in respect of *Clinical Studies in Psychiatry* by Harry Stack Sullivan; the author in respect of 'Analogy in Science' by Dr Robert Oppenheimer; The Oxford University Press in respect of *The Basic Works of Aristotle* edited by Richard McKeon; Prentice-Hall Inc. in respect of *Ethical Theories* edited by A. I. Melden (Copyright 1955); Princeton University Press in respect of *How to Solve It* by G. Polya (Copyright 1945); Random House Inc. in respect of *The English*

Acknowledgements

Philosophers from Bacon to Mill edited by Edwin A. Burtt; Charles Scribner's Sons in respect of *Descartes Selections* edited by Ralph M. Eaton, *Plato: The Republic* edited by C. M. Baker, *The Theory of the Business Enterprise* by Thorstein Veblen, *Spinoza Selections* edited by John Wild; The University of California Press in respect of *The Creative Process* edited by Brewster Ghiselin; George Wittenborn, Inc., in respect of *Life of Forms in Art* by Henri Focillon; Yale University Press in respect of *Ethics and Language* by Charles Stevenson.

INTRODUCTION

When I began to work on this book some three years ago, I wanted to make sense of a radical shift in environment and task. I had moved from studying and teaching philosophy to working as an industrial consultant. As a student and teacher I had been concerned, among other things, with theories of discovery, theories of the mind, theories of deciding, and theories of the social process. As an industrial consultant for the last four years I have been trying to help to develop new products for client companies and to help these companies to make more effective use of their own resources for technical innovation. The germ of this book was the notion that the evolution of theories is very much like processes of invention and product development as they occur in industry; that the two kinds of development can be seen as embodiments of a single underlying process, which I call the displacement of concepts.

Aspects of the displacement of concepts have been discussed, in several areas of discipline, under the headings of metaphor and analogy. In at least one of its senses, the process of metaphor is nothing more or less than my displacement of concepts. But, in general, metaphor and analogy have been treated as ornaments of language or as types of meaning peculiar to aesthetics. For me, on the other hand, the displacement of concepts is central to the development of all new concepts and theories, whether they have to do with science, invention, or philosophy. The process is nothing less than our way of bringing the familiar to bear on the unfamiliar, in such a way as to yield new concepts while at the same time retaining as much as possible of the past.

This is, certainly, a sweeping and monolithic view. It began with mere exploration of the role of metaphor in the formation of new concepts, but in no time at all metaphor, like King Charles's head, monopolized the work. I now find it difficult to see the formation of new concepts in any terms other than the displacement of concepts. Rather than struggle against the urge, I have tried to make a virtue of the defect and have pushed the explanation as far as I can push it. The result is a thesis which is certainly false in its over-simplification. Nevertheless, it presents one way of looking at the subject strongly, and I hope evocatively.

The book is in two major parts, one dealing with the 'radical' function of the displacement of concepts in the formation of new concepts and the other with its 'conservative' function in retaining the patterns of old concepts. There are six chapters, whose contents are roughly as follows:

Chapter I sets out to look at the question of the emergence of new concepts and theories. There have been many attempts to answer the question, ranging from the works of Plato to those of Poincaré. Most of them fall into one of two categories: they claim either that novelty in theories is illusory and needs no explanation or that it is mysterious and permits no explanation.

Chapter II attempts a new tack. It begins with the notion that the emergence of a new concept involves, in some sense, treating the new in terms of the old. After all, we have nothing else. But the processes which would seem at first to involve treatment of the new in terms of the old (for example, comparison, and the correct or incorrect application of a concept to an instance) turn out not to have to do with the formation of new concepts. In these cases the old concepts are used but do not change. There is another kind of process, however, in which an old concept is shifted to a new situation in such a way as to change and to extend itself. I give some examples of this process and call it the displacement of concepts. It bears some relation to what we ordinarily think of as metaphor or analogy.

In *Chapter III* metaphor and analogy are discussed. But these terms, as they are usually defined, preclude the emergence of novelty. Only Cassirer, to my knowledge, avoids both the trap of excluding metaphor as non-scientific and therefore meaningless and the trap of roping off metaphorical truth as a separate kind of truth distinguishable from and opposed to scientific truth. He expresses the view I want to defend: that processes of metaphor, or the displacement of concepts, are essential processes in the development of new theories, scientific or otherwise.

Chapter IV provides a closer look at this remarkable process, pointing out a number of distinguishable phases: transposition of aspects of the old theory to the new situation; their interpretation in the new situation; correction, with respect to what is new in the new situation; and spelling out of the areas of community and difference between the old and the transposed theory. Each process of displacement revolves around the establishment of symbolic relations between the old theory and the new situation. The symbolic relation cannot be understood as a 'similarity of relations'—which is, as I understand it, an after-the-fact view. It seems to consist in the old theory's coming to function as a projective model for the new situation. In every case we are asked to 'find the old theory in the new situation' and in the process of doing so we come to see the old theory, too, in a different way.

Theories are selected for displacement on a number of bases: the gifts of the various overlapping cultures involved, the metaphors underlying the ready-made theories in terms of which the new situations are already partly structured, and the demands of those new situations—that is, the aptness of the old theory, taken as a projective model, to provide new solutions for the problematic aspects of those situations.

These new solutions—hypotheses or 'ideas'—come out of our attempts to find projective equivalents for aspects of the old theory in the new situation. Examples of this process are drawn from cases of product development and invention and from the history of science. It is illustrated in the teaching of geometry. These processes may be extremely complex; a single process of invention may embody a series of displacements, on the analogy of a theme and variations, each step serving as projective model for what follows. The process has an emotional foundation and a dramatic structure of its own. Our understanding of the process shows signs of contributing, in a limited way, to a heuristic of invention and discovery.

This focus on invention and discovery does not do justice to the scope of the displacement of concepts in our lives. To correct this, I attempt to relate it to generalization, to perception, to behavioural learning, and most of all to our language. The metaphors of our language seem to me to be signs of the historical displacement of concepts.

Chapter V presents the displacement of concepts in its conservative role. It can be seen as the means by which we retain as much as possible of the old in our adaptation to the new. By way of illustration, a number of theories held in formal writings and in common sense are considered: theories of deciding, theories of the mind, theories of understanding, and theories of romantic love. In each case I attempt to show that the language of the theory contains metaphors—metaphors of the scale, the use of tools, social processes, government, mechanism and dynamism, atomism, vision, Christianity—which signify the displacement of older theories which had functioned as projective models for the theory in question. These metaphors go hand in hand with assumptions, transposed sometimes in a covert and uncritical way, whose presence in the theory they help to explain. Attention to metaphor functions in this way as a useful analytical tool.

Since the theories considered are drawn from different historical periods, there begin to emerge in *Chapter VI* some hints of the historical displacement of theories. These patterns of displacement represent what amounts to a 'life of metaphor in theory' which parallels, in a gigantic way, the patterns of displacement in individual processes of invention and discovery.

Of the material summarized above, I owe more than I would care to admit to marathon conversations held over the last four years with people I was lucky enough to find at Arthur D. Little,

Inc. Among these are Dr Raymond Hainer, Robert Jolkovski, W. J. J. Gordon, Paul Matisse, Sherman Kingsbury, and David Gleicher. They hold no responsibility for the distortions I have introduced in trying to make a book of it all.

PART ONE

The Radical Function

CHAPTER I

Asking the Question:
A Review of some Theories of
the Formation of New Concepts

People have been trying to explain the emergence of new concepts for over two thousand years. Writers of almost every kind have been at one time or another concerned with it: philosophers, theologians, psychologists, physical scientists, poets. The history of their theories ranges from Plato to Saint Augustine, from Bacon and Descartes to Hartley, Hobbes, Locke, and Hume; from the Romantic poets of the nineteenth century to Bergson, Freud, and the Gestalt psychologists. In our own time the body of literature on the subject has reached epic proportions. American industry, for its own reasons, has developed a kind of manic preoccupation with the subject and many writers from the academic world, largely in one or another of the social sciences, have reflected industry's concern.

In spite of the abundance of the literature and the innumerable contributions that have been made, theories on the subject fall into one of two categories: either they make the process mysterious, and therefore intrinsically unexplainable; or they regard novelty as illusory and, therefore, requiring no explanation. These themes are readily apparent in writings from Plato's time. In our own time they are less apparent but equally powerful.

This division reflects a similar division in the history of attempts to account for metaphysical novelty, novelty in the world itself. In both cases the tendency either to obscurantize or to explain away novelty reflects the great difficulty of explaining it. The difficulty comes in large part from our inclination, with things and thoughts alike, to take an after-the-fact view. This after-the-fact-ness in theories of the formation of new concepts has tended to keep from investigation a kind of process which is central to this subject matter: the process of metaphor or, as I will call it, the displacement of concepts.

In this chapter some of the dominant theories of new concept formation will be examined, illustrating the division mentioned above. Some exceptions will be noted as well. I will need to begin, however, with comments about the notion of 'new concept' itself.

NEW CONCEPTS

It would be comforting at this point to be able to offer a definition of 'new concept' which would carry through the capsule history proposed in this chapter and through the rest of the book. Unfortunately, the writers to be discussed use 'new concept' in many different, and some inconsistent, ways. The most that can be done, therefore, is to make some of the crucial distinctions and to block out some of the areas of the subject that will be of greatest interest.

I want to use the word 'concept' broadly enough to include a child's first notion of his mother, our notion of the cold war, my daughter's concept of a thing-game, Ralph Ellison's idea of the Negro as an invisible man, the Newtonian theory of light, and the idea of a new mechanical fastener.

These are all concepts as we ordinarily use the term, and as I want to use it. Whether they are to be regarded exclusively as language, behaviour, images, logical terms, or the like, is not the issue. These are all ways of looking at concepts which may from time to time be useful. However, there is an underlying model

4

for our thinking about concepts which is at once quite general and quite harmful. It has a traditional place in philosophy and psychology and it is enshrined in our language.

When we say that we 'have' a concept, that it is 'applied' to an instance, that it 'fits' or does not 'fit' that instance, we speak as though a concept were a kind of concrete thing. We speak of 'big' and 'little' ideas, 'my' idea and 'yours', 'few' or 'many' ideas. We spatialize ideas. We give them a certain generality—a single idea may 'apply' to many instances—but we speak as though they had definite limits and could be handled like spatial things. It is as though we thought of concepts as mental stencils superimposed on experience.

This way of thinking is characteristic of traditional logic, in which concepts are thought to refer to sets of properties (the 'intension' or 'connotation' of a term) which define classes of objects. These classes may be related to one another by inclusion, exclusion, overlapping, or any of the kinds of relation permitted by the familiar Venn diagrams.

While the Venn diagrams are a technique for manipulating concepts in their logical relations, they are also a symbol of the essentially spatial way in which concepts, in traditional logic, are conceived. As Bergson showed, this makes change of concept, the dynamic character of concepts generally, almost impossible to imagine.

Fortunately, there is, in writers like Dewey, C. I. Lewis, and Wittgenstein, another way of looking at concepts. Here concepts are seen as tools for coping with the world, for solving problems.

In our ordinary commerce with the world, we come to generate certain expectations. In the laboratory a new liquid is discovered. It is transparent, viscous, corrosive to the touch. We form a certain sensory Gestalt of it. Gradually, in our dealings with it, we learn what to expect. It flows in certain ways under certain conditions, it behaves in certain ways when heated, it combines with various compounds, it has certain characteristic reactions to radiation and so on. In our learning, we are able to relate it to many other familiar concepts. This, in a shorthand way, provides us with many other expectations. Our concept of the liquid is just this learning about it, just this set of funded expectations. It is indefinitely great, fuzzy at the edges, and constantly changing.

Language is an internalized stimulus for this body of expectations. When I say, to others or to myself, 'This is an acid' or generally 'This is an x', I awaken these expectations. I am able to deal with the thing. I can bring to bear what I have learned to expect of it.

This way of thinking about concepts, as Dewey showed at great length in his *Logic* (1938), relates our conceptual behaviour to animal learning generally. The verbal side of a concept is shorthand for our learning about an area of experience. This shorthand, these expectations, are things we *use* in our commerce with the world, and they can be understood and evaluated in ways analogous to our understanding and evaluation of other things we use. This much Dewey and Wittgenstein have in common.

C. I. Lewis (1946) has formalized this view in his theory of judgement. Every judgement about an object he analyses into a series of judgements, indefinitely long, each of which is of the form, 'Given a certain sense experience, if I act in a certain way, then I can expect to be presented with certain other sense experiences.' It is always only arbitrarily that I bring to an end the list of expectations associated with my concept of a thing.

From this point of view, the 'intension' and 'extension' of a term are abstracted from the expectations and behaviour which make up a concept. They are taken, as it were, from the outside. If we observe the situations in which we use a term and bring into play the expectations associated with it, we begin to enumerate its extension. If we choose from the mass of expectations involved those which characterize all and only cases in which the term is used, we give its intension. In formal systems, the attempt is made to limit concepts to their extensions and intensions. Otherwise we must understand intension and extension as limited and rather arbitrary selections from among the expectations that make up the concept and the conditions under which they are brought into play.

It is sometimes useful and interesting to abstract concepts from the situations in which they are used. They have generality in the sense in which tools have generality. They may be used in more than one situation. Abstracted from their situations of use, they can be looked at as forms or Gestalts. They are, in this sense, structures developed in our experience and they are entirely analogous to perceptual forms. Of the many points that could be made about this Gestalt character of concepts, I want to emphasize the following:

The situations we conceive in a certain way can be conceived in an indefinite variety of other ways as well. This fact stares us in the face whenever we look at what happens in the formation of new concepts, even though the inertia of our conceptual systems, once established, is so great as to make us almost incredulous about it. A lamp is a lamp, after all. A typewriter is a typewriter. It is a great advantage of the famous Gestalt figures that they make the point vivid and stubborn.

1. is a staircase, or an overhanging ledge.

2. is a bird or a rabbit.

3. is a vase, or two faces in profile.

Once having resolved a problematic area of experience, once having found a way of looking at (and therefore dealing with) a situation which was at first novel and puzzling, our impulse to stick with it is overwhelmingly powerful. We have 'adapted' to it, and through it. Our concept-forming apparatus operates under a categorical imperative of 'let well enough alone'. It is at once a reflection of this tendency, and a protection of it, that we are apt to regard our ways of looking at things as inherent and immutable in the things themselves. But the formation of new concepts always requires us to break these settled ways of looking at things, to 'come apart' with respect to them, prior to the formation of a new concept.

Given what has been said above, concepts are to be distinguished from their instances, from the situations to which they apply. But this is a distinction rather than a separation. At a given time, everything is what it is in terms of the concept or Gestalt under which it is understood. There are no things without concepts. It is only by a process of abstraction that we distinguish between concept-tools and the situations in which they are used. While a given situation can be conceived in a variety of ways, it is always a *concept-structured situation*. There are no observations, data, perceptions, objects, independent of concepts. We cannot even name things without giving clues to the concepts which make 'things' of the situations confronting us.

This point is far from original. It has characterized modern thinking about us and the world, from Kant's 'Copernican revolution' to contemporary theory of knowledge. Its special importance here is that it puts our inquiry in its proper perspective: to ask about the formation of new concepts is to ask about the process by which we discover the character of the world.

If we understand concepts as the fund of expectations in terms of which we structure our experience, it becomes clear that concepts and theories cannot be separated. My concept of a lamp is my theory of a lamp, in the sense in which 'theory' means the set of propositions, expectations, insights, that enables me to deal with it. Only in formal systems, again, do we have any luck in distinguishing between concepts and theories. There we can talk about a term, formally limited to a certain intension, and the propositions in which that term appears. In our actual inquiry into the world, however, we can only talk about overlapping theories. Isolated 'concepts', as formally used, are abstracted from theories. The common idea that theories are 'built out of' concepts reverses the real process.

Wittgenstein expresses this when he says that concepts are theory-laden. Our idea of 'pawn' carries with it and depends for its sense upon the idea of the game of chess. The concept of 'mass' is part and parcel of our concept of Newtonian physics. To ask about the formation of new concepts, again, is to ask about the formation of new theories, or still again, to ask about the formation of new sets of expectations for dealing with the world.

'New concept', like 'concept', is another of those deceptively simple common-sense terms.

In its most general sense a new concept, like any new thing, is what comes up for the first time. For a child the idea of a circus is at some time new. For most adults the ideas of planned obsolescence, the population explosion, escalation, the genetic code, are still relatively new. Learning is interaction with new concepts. Because a new concept is one that comes up for the first time, it is unexpected. It is subject to a special sort of attention and comes to be perceived like a figure against the background of familiar and therefore relatively unnoticed situations.

Concepts are always new with respect to a variety of things. We can no more talk about intrinsic novelty than we can talk about intrinsic parenthood, since concepts may be new in some respects and old in others. It is worth spelling out some of these distinctions in kinds of novelty.

Perhaps most significant is the distinction between a new concept and a new concept of 'this'. Suppose you have an old friend who has hidden from you the fact that he is a Mason. When you hear of this for the first time, your notion of the man changes— but not your notion of Masons. You had a notion of Masons before you knew that he was one of them. Again, a chemist tests a liquid, and finds that it is an organic solvent. He forms a new concept of the liquid, but the notion of organic solvent is an old one for him and does not change in this process. In both cases, what is new is the first identification of a specific thing as an instance of an old concept. The concept itself does not change except in the trivial sense of being found applicable to one more instance.

On the other hand, there are concepts in chemistry—like 'stereo-regular polymer'—which are new for the culture of chemistry as well as for the specific things to which they are applied. When a child first stumbles on the notion of infinity— as the concept of a series 'that you can't come to the end of'—the concept is new for him and not just for the things or numbers with which he is concerned in his discovery of it. New concepts in this sense are my concern in this book.

I have hinted at the distinction between a concept that is new for an individual and one that is new for his culture. The child's notion of infinity was new for him but not for his culture; the chemist's notion of stereo-regular polymers was new for his culture as well—like such ideas of our time as the cold war, atomic fission, and the population explosion. Since concept formation is very much alike in discovery and rediscovery, I will be looking at concepts new for an individual whether they are new for his culture or not.

New concepts grow out of what has gone before and can be seen as changes in the old. But these changes are matters of degree. In some cases the new concept is recognizable as a minor variation of an old one, as in the case of the derivation of 'superjet' from 'jet'. In other cases the new concept's connection with the old may be obscure, as in the case of the emergence of Marx's notion of a classless society or Bohr's idea of a quantum leap.

The concepts that strike us as least like the old are by and large those which require greatest change in the old. Our conceptual structure can be seen as a kind of amoeba. In the centre are the concepts most crucial, most intimately tied to others, least willingly let go. Nearer the periphery are concepts less intimately tied to others, less crucial to the whole system, less jealously guarded. 'Umpire', 'horsemanship', 'window-dressing', are examples of the latter kind. 'Cause', 'health', 'success', are examples of the former. This distinction between central and peripheral concepts bears on the question of degree of novelty. The more central the changing concept, the newer in this sense it is.

Degree of novelty may refer, therefore, to the recency of the concept's emergence, to the ease with which it can be traced to old concepts, or to the degree of centrality of the concept changed. Of these, the last is particularly important in bodies of more or less formal theory, like science and technology, where determining degree of novelty is often a matter of practical concern. The more change involved in the acceptance of a new theory, the more radically new it is found to be and, usually, the more vigorously it is resisted. Recently developed notions of parity in physics or of molecular configuration (as in Pauling's theories of protein structure), are viewed as radically new; whereas the identification of a new isotope of carbon or a new value of π are not. Acceptance of the former would require changing much accepted theory in nuclear physics or in protein chemistry, whereas acceptance of the latter requires little change at all.

For me, then, new concepts are those which emerge for the first time for an individual whether they are new for his culture or not. They are new in themselves for the individual, and not merely a new concept of some thing. Their acceptance makes for a radical change in familiar theory.

These distinctions begin to raise, rather than to resolve, the question of what new concepts and new concept formation are about. They are intended as preparation for the capsule history that follows.

THEORIES OF NEW CONCEPT FORMATION

In spite of the many angles from which new concepts have been considered, it is striking how theories of the matter tend to group themselves into one of two camps: those which make a mystery of the emergence of new concepts and those which reduce new concepts to old.

The situation is entirely parallel to the case of theories of the emergence of new things. Throughout the history of philosophy, writers have tended to join either those who treat the emergence of novelty as creation *ex nihilo* and therefore a mystery, or those who treat novelty as illusory and maintain that things remain essentially the same. The Eleatics and Heraclitus, the mechanists and Bergson, Spinoza and Descartes, represent these opposite positions. The motive of the 'conservative' side has been to explain everything, excluding the new as disruptive; and the 'radical' side may very well have been moved by the wish to destroy the old conceptual order by rendering everything inexplicable.

THEORIES OF MYSTERY

These treat novelty as absolute and, to the extent that 'cause' implies understandability in principle, they treat it as causeless. They attribute the emergence of new concepts to an inscrutable agency and can be distinguished according to what they have said about that agency: Plato in the *Ion* presents a theory of divine inspiration—a breath from the Gods producing a divine madness shared alike by Socrates and the poets. In medieval Christianity inspiration becomes revelation. The metaphors are different: a breath from the outside, an outside light revealed. Both require communication from an outer, unknowable agency.

There is a pantheistic mystic strain (Plotinus, certain medieval mystics, Bruno) in which the agency becomes a world spirit, an Everything. In romanticism this world spirit is identified with nature. The romantic notion of the artist alone, away from society, drawing his inspiration from nature, comes in part from this source.

Certain theories of the unconscious seem to belong to the same category. At least since Graham Wallas (1926), in the early part

of this century, it has been commonplace to refer to the unconscious as the source of new ideas. It is one thing to use the
notion of the unconscious operationally as a way of explaining
events, like delayed remembering; but it is another matter to
treat it as an outside agency, powerful but unknowable, from
which ideas come. When reference to the unconscious is treated
as the ending, rather than the beginning of inquiry, theories of the
unconscious become theories of mystery.

All of these theories take the thing they are trying to explain
and put a mystery in place of their inability to explain it. What
stops inquiry is not the idea of an outside agency transmitting new
concepts to man, but the inscrutability attributed to that agency.
Actually, the idea of transmission from the outside helps to
account for some features of the emergence of new concepts: the
sense of unexpectedness, independence of will, the sense of a gift.
But the process of transmission is made mysterious. And the
problem of explanation is merely shifted: the thing that is transmitted, how did it come to be formed in the first place?

THEORIES OF REDUCTION

Theories which are not mysterious avoid the problem of explaining new concepts by denying that there is anything essentially
new to explain.

One family of theories, associationism, treats a new idea as a
simple, lawlike recombination of old ideas. In the writings of
Hartley, Locke, Hume, and on in some quarters to the present
day, there are certain simple, primitive ideas (colour, shape,
extension, number, among others). All more complex ideas,
including 'new' ones, are additive combinations of these simple
ones. Moreover, each recombination is lawlike. Ideas combine on
the basis of frequency of conjunction, similarity, contrast, or the
like. Ideas combine additively; there is nothing in the new wholes
that was not in the old parts. The conditions of the new wholes are
given either in externally imposed conjunction or in fixed relations
of similarity and difference. Pushed to an extreme, the formation

of new concepts must be viewed as externally conditioned by the imposed temporal conjunction of events.

Much of this is retained in more recent stimulus-response psychology, drawing from the conditioned response theory of Pavlov and the behaviourism of Watson. Here the elements to be combined are units of behaviour, rather than mental events known as ideas. In strict versions of the theory, concepts are treated as patterns of association of stimulus and response. But again, complex responses are viewed as having been constructed, according to a few basic laws, from simple ones. 'New' associations of stimulus and response come about either through the accident of temporal conjunction, later reinforced, or through external training.

Both theories represent versions of psychological atomism. Just as matter can be seen as made up of such unalterable units, always the same and always interacting according to a few immutable laws; so concepts, however conceived, can be seen as lawful combinations of conceptual atoms. In the conceptual, as in the material, realm, there is nothing new to explain.

In some modern views the plot remains the same but the locale shifts to the unconscious. Thus, Poincaré describes the emergence of new concepts as follows:

> Figure the future elements of our combinations as something like the hooked atoms of Epicurus . . . during a period of apparent rest and unconscious work, certain of them are detached from the wall and put in motion . . . Then their mutual impacts may produce new combinations (Poincaré, 1955, p. 41).

Here the atomic metaphor is explicit. New combinations are randomly produced from certain pre-selected mental elements. Once produced, they are screened. The conscious part of the process is primarily a screening process, in fact. It consists in work on new combinations rather than in the *formation* of anything new.

Exploration of the creative process in terms of computers tends

14

to move along similar lines. Bits of information are fed into the machine, randomly combined, screened, and subjected to logical operations. All attempts to explore computer 'learning' have, so far, incorporated random recombination of elements. Speed, the sheer number of combinations made and tested, is supposed to compensate for the apparent inefficiency of the process.

The difficulties with this kind of theory run as follows:

1. As the Gestalt writers have shown, new ideas cannot be viewed as additive combinations of old ones. The atomic analogy breaks down. The idea of a cold war is not the idea of cold added to the idea of war. The best argument proceeds through examples showing that the perceptual or conceptual whole is more than the sum of its parts, that the addition or subtraction of an element makes changes which are far more than additive.

2. The notion of simple, primitive conceptual or perceptual elements is also suspect. Simplicity and primitiveness break down outside of formal systems, and perhaps even within them. Wittgenstein and his followers have shown that supposedly simple concepts are theory-laden.

3. All versions of the associationist theory hold that new ideas are mechanical recombinations of old simple ideas, where recombination is either externally imposed or random and therefore requires no psychological or logical explanation. The screening of ideas is the explainable part. But this neglects the emergence of new screening concepts. The development of new criteria for solution of the problem is often key to development of new concepts. Moreover, the mechanical separation of generation and screening functions is false to the process as it happens. It is most often out of the interaction of specific ideas and screening categories, and their mutual change, that new concepts arise.

There is an analogy here to a common view of the matter in industry. The generation of new product ideas is supposed to occur by itself or to be inexplicable. What is considered important is the collection and screening of ideas. Ideas tend to be regarded as ready-made and complete, fit for selection or rejection, and the criteria for selection are likewise considered fixed. Here as in associationist views, no room is left for the mutual change essential to new concept formation.

Theories of mystery and reduction are not always so readily identifiable. There are two additional bodies of theory, Gestalt theory and theories of scientific method, where the mysterious and reductionist aspects are less obvious.

THE GESTALT VIEW

The Gestalt school of psychology has regularly criticized associationist attempts to explain new concepts as additive recombinations of old ones. Gestalt writers like Wertheimer, Koffka, and Köhler, have insisted on the organic and dynamic, rather than mechanical, character of the process. Beginning with studies of perception, they have extended their findings to conceptual fields as well.

For them, the emergence of new concepts, when it occurs in the context of a specific problem-solving situation, is called Insight. It is treated as the sudden reorganization of a perceptual or conceptual field.

In *The Mentality of Apes* (1948) Köhler is intent on showing that the problem-solving behaviour of apes represents Insight in this sense rather than mere chance combinations of elements of behaviour, reinforced by success. In *Gestalt Psychology* (1947) he addresses himself again to the nature of Insight, without raising the question of novelty as such. His main point is that certain causal relations in experience are neither learned nor arrived at by induction but are matters of direct awareness. He limits his discussion to causal relations between 'experienced fact' and 'inner response' (like the taste of beer and pleasure in the taste), but his remarks are presumably applicable (although this is unclear) to relations of experienced facts alone. He implies that at least some of the new solutions discovered by the apes are to be understood as direct experience of relations between experienced facts in the situation. Wertheimer, in *Productive Thinking* (1945), makes a similar point about the appearance of new solutions in the problem-solving efforts of human beings.

This reference to 'direct experience' is meant to counter associationist or inductive theories of discovery. But is it also meant to imply that there is nothing further to be explained about the emergence of new concepts? At times both Köhler and Wertheimer seem to say this. In Köhler's work, the problem at this point is made to shift to the relation between experienced causal relations and parallel 'cortical processes' which require the development of a 'Gestalt Biology'.

The Gestalt writers seem to me, without realizing it, to treat insight as a kind of inner sight in which new relations of fact are directly apprehended, as it were by vision. Oddly enough, in their treatment of visual perception they insist on the importance of the active contribution of the perceiver through his conceptual structuring of the perceived situation. Is the emergence of new conceptual structures to be treated in terms of a direct passive awareness of fact which is denied at the visual level itself?

In Gestalt theory what is presented is the inadequacy of reductionist theories and the need for attention to insight, but insight itself remains mysterious.

THEORIES OF SCIENTIFIC METHOD

In his *Novum Organum* Sir Francis Bacon treats new concepts in science as numerical generalizations about particular events. His theories have been so thoroughly criticized by later exponents of scientific method that I need say little about them here. Scientific inquiry hardly ever has the form of simple numerical induction ('All these crows are black'); and, in any case, this theory presupposes rather than explains the new term (if it is new) which is applied to the particulars examined.

17

The idea of scientific method which has dominated philosophy of science for the last several hundred years can be described as the hypothetico-deductive theory. According to it, the scientific method consists in making observations, forming hypotheses to explain them, deducing consequences from these hypotheses, and performing experiments to confirm or disconfirm the hypotheses. It has been common among philosophers of science to regard the emergence of new hypotheses as relevant only in so far as the logic of their evaluation is concerned. The actual coming into being of new hypotheses has been relegated to the psychologists (who have treated it, in general, along the lines mentioned above). This has been true even of the few contemporary philosophers of science concerned with the logic of discovery. For Hanson (1958) and Popper (1959), for example, the logic of discovery turns out to mean the logic of justification of new hypotheses in science.

An exception is to be made for those theorists of science who have dealt with the role of analogy in the formation of new hypotheses. This group includes Oppenheimer. For him new hypotheses come about through a process of analogy which he interprets as application of old hypotheses to new situations and correction to account for the difference. As in theories where new concept formation is seen as random combination of old elements plus 'screening', what is in question here is something old and an apparently understandable operation on it. So Oppenheimer (1956) looks at wave theory, originally developed for liquids, as having been 'applied' to light; then one had to 'find the disanalogy' which enables one to preserve what was right about the analogy'. The disanalogies were, among other things, the notion that wave-properties applied to changes in states of energy rather than to flowing mass, and that the same phenomena adequately described as wave phenomena in some respects could also be adequately described in other respects as particulate.

A question should be raised here about this notion of 'correction'. Oppenheimer appears to see correction in terms of trimming a pattern to fit an original. The shape of the original is given, the pattern need only be cut to fit; no invention is needed. But in the sense in which this explanation demands it, there is no 'original' for the new concept. The situation does not impose a new form, of which the new concept is an imitation. The new concept, in terms of which the new situation is being structured is itself in process of formation. There is an alternative here, according to which new concepts can be seen as imitations, passive registrations, of new forms in nature. Such a view fits certain writings of Aristotle, but it is incongruent with current views of perception and cognition which give to the perceiver an active role in structuring what is known.

And where does the new hypothesis, the correcting one, come from?—for example, the theory of the wave-like behaviour of changes in states of energy? Is the mistaken part of the old hypothesis of any help in coming to the new one?—is the mistake simply what has to be excised and replaced? If the mistake helps, how can this help be accounted for?

The difficulty seems to be that Oppenheimer reduces the relations involved to concept-instance relations. He is always literally *applying* an old to a new, and changing the old. *Finding* the change he does not deal with. But the new idea does not spring full blown from the disconfirmation of the old hypothesis. No amount of 'experience' can provide it, unless the right question is asked. And the genesis of the right question is still mysterious.

This opposition of mysterious and reductionist theories holds in several areas beside philosophical and psychological theories of new concept formation. It can be found in the history of thought where some writers (like Harry Wolfson, 1958) delight in showing how each supposedly 'new' doctrine can be shown to be a trivial modification of a passage in Avicenna which is, in turn, a version of a thesis in Aristotle; while other writers take equal pleasure in pointing out the sudden and mysterious appearance of radically new theory. A similar split can be found in theories of history and, more particularly, in the history of technology where some authors (Gilfillan, 1935, is one) stress the fact that invention is the cumulative result of innumerable increments of least perceptible change, while others regard the history of invention as a series of conceptual leaps, essentially inexplicable, each opening up a vein of technology. The attitudes of individual inventors and researchers are apt to vary in an analogous way. Some take pains to point out the old ideas of which their theories are simply rediscoveries, while others stress the essential mystery and uniqueness of the invention.

These differences are not merely academic. They have psychological functions for the inventor or researcher—presenting him to himself as a 'magic creator' or a man safely buried in the past. And they have social consequences for new invention or new theory. Depending on the context, it is not a matter of indifference, as far as acceptance is concerned, whether a theory is presented as essentially new or essentially old.

While this apposition between mysterious and reductionist theories is very common, my chief point is that it is not exhaustive. By way of contrast, I would like to explore ways of looking at the emergence of new concepts which show how they are derived from old ones to which they are still not reduced.

My use of the word 'emergence' in connection with new concepts indicates that my own metaphors will be drawn from evolutionary biology. But 'evolution', if it is treated in this connection as an explanation rather than as something to be explained, is an empty cliché.

My chief difficulty is in our tendency to understand the business of forming new concepts in a vocabulary that is appropriate only to their justification *after the fact*. We are used to thinking about fully formulated concepts, their relations to one another and to their instances. As long as we focus on the concept-instance relation, we will be at a loss to understand the formation of new concepts. It is as though we tried to understand the emergence of new species in terms of our concepts of existing species, their relations to one another and to their members. We will be forced to think of the newness of new concepts as either illusory or mysterious.

But is it possible to make an attack on the vocabulary of after-the-fact justification intelligible when our very criteria for intelligibility depend on that vocabulary?

My attempt begins with the following chapter.

CHAPTER II

Starting from Scratch:
Treating the New in Terms of the Old

If we abandon the after-the-fact view of concept formation and the corollary notion that new concepts are either illusory or mysterious, what have we left? Where can we begin?

We are left, I think, with the observation that in working towards the new, we have nothing to use but the old. In Oppenheimer's words, 'We cannot, coming into something new, deal with it except on the basis of the familiar and the old-fashioned . . .' (Oppenheimer, 1956).

But this truism is paradoxical: consider the story of Epaminondas, who spoiled the cake he was carrying from his Auntie to his Mammy.

'Cake!' said his Mammy. 'Epaminondas, you ain't got the sense you was born with! That's no way to carry cake. The way to carry cake is to wrap it all up nice in some leaves and put it in your hat, and put your hat on your head, and come along home. You hear me, Epaminondas?'

'Yes, Mammy,' said Epaminondas.

Next day Epaminondas went to see his Auntie and she gave him a pound of butter for his Mammy—fine, fresh, sweet, butter.

Epaminondas wrapped it up in leaves and put it in his hat and came along home.

It was a very hot day. Pretty soon the butter began to melt. It melted and melted and as it melted it ran down Epaminondas' forehead; then it ran over his face, and in his ears and down his neck. When he got home, all the butter Epaminondas had was *on him*. His Mammy looked at him and then she said:

'Law's sake! Epaminondas, what you got in your hat?'

'Butter, Mammy,' said Epaminondas; 'Auntie gave it to me.'

'Butter!' said his Mammy. 'Epaminondas, you ain't got the sense you was born with! . . .' (Bryant, 1938, pp. 6–8).

The paradox in the notion that you cannot deal with the new except on the basis of the old is that this is also a definition of *un*intelligence. Epaminondas treats each new situation as though it were exactly like the one he had just learned how to cope with. He deals with novelty by ignoring it.

While this is a rather human way of dealing with novelty, and the way most of us deal with it most of the time, it is not the way new concepts are formed. If we cannot deal with the new except on the basis of the old, there are nevertheless ways and ways of doing it. When we are intelligent in dealing with the new we deal with it as, on the basis of, through, or in terms of the old, still without reducing it to the old. But what does it mean to do this?

We are figurative rather than literal. We are approximate rather than exact. We use analogy.

These phrases are descriptive without being adequate. There are several ways in which we treat the new as the old. There are several ways in which we treat one thing as another. But how are these processes related to the formation of new concepts?

COMPARISON

Comparison involves a juxtaposition of one thing and another, sometimes of old and new. It is the word most generally used when metaphor and analogy are defined.

Let us compare the USSR and the United States. (How regularly we deal with *two* things when comparison is in question, as though all comparison involved two hands!) Both countries are enormous in size and population. Both are industrial giants. Both are the products of violent revolutions. But in the USSR revolution has come more recently and at a time when its middle class was far less well developed and its technology more infantile.

A comparison, in so far as this example is typical, is a ticking off of characteristics, those in respect to which the two things are similar and those in respect to which they are different.

Often it is evaluative. Children compare shells to see which is prettier or shinier. They compare themselves to see who is bigger or smarter. Comparison reveals how two things stand with respect to given characteristics. Comparison establishes relationships.

But the characteristics under which things are compared do not originate with the comparison. In order to say how things stand in relation to a characteristic, we must already have the concept of the characteristic—as we have, above, the concepts of size, population, industrial giant, and the like. As far as these concepts are concerned, they leave the comparison as they entered it. No new concepts emerge.

There is a sense in which *something* new emerges, however. We may notice for the first time that the USSR and the United States are products of revolution.

The process by which we come to do so is interesting. We ordinarily begin a comparison confident of having in mind all of the relevant characteristics of the two things, just as we have in mind the forms of two children that we need only 'see together' to compare. But the demands of symmetry implicit in comparison may force us to see for the first time how one of the two things is an instance of a concept which we had applied before only to the other. Or we may notice for the first time that the two things are similar or different in a certain respect, even though we had been used to thinking of each separately, in terms of that characteristic.

There is a trivial sense here in which the relationship discovered may be said to be new. But if we find for the first time that the USSR and the United States are similar in being revolutionary, neither 'similar' nor 'revolutionary' is a new concept for us. All that may be new for us is the thought that the two countries are together instances of these concepts. Comparison is still an establishing of some or different, more or less, with respect to concepts already in use.

Strictly speaking, then, comparison cannot be a way of treating the new as the old. We cannot compare the new with the old, just because the new—in so far as it is new—is not yet formed, not yet concept-structured. The apparent exceptions that come to mind turn out to be comparisons of the old with the less old or comparisons of the old with the new in so far as it is old. This is the pity of all those laborious, systematic comparisons with which a certain kind of mind (I think of it, with some prejudice, as the Germanic mind) struggles in order to come to novelty. Comparison by itself never produces anything significantly new.

It is true, however, that the formation of a new concept is often something to which a comparison leads. Through having noticed that the USSR and the United States were founded in revolution, we may go on to try to discover how the similarities and differences in their histories can be attributed to that origin, and the effort may lead us to a concept, new for us, of a revolution-founded nation. Or, in seeking for a Russian middle class to juxtapose with ours, we may be confronted with a class of individuals both like and unlike our middle class, requiring a new concept. The very pattern of similarities and differences uncovered in a comparison may provide the raw material for a new concept. But this new material must be structured through the attempt to bring it to other situations. A chemist's 'curves', an anthropologist's 'profiles', develop in this way.

'Comparison' may refer to the process of ticking off similarities and differences; to the results of the process; to the ranking process or to the simple juxtaposing of two things so that something else can be accomplished. It is in this last sense that comparison is most interesting. Seeing two things together lets us come to judgements about bigger, taller, smaller, brighter, same, and different. Juxtaposing the old and the new, so that they can be 'seen as one', is in some sense a condition for the formation of new concepts. But the formation of new concepts goes well beyond this juxtaposition.

Charles Peirce somewhere gives this definition of error: it consists in treating different things as though they were similar or the same things as though they were different. On the basis of this definition, the formation of new concepts treating the new as the old can perhaps best be understood as a form of error. Coming to form a new concept involves in several ways making a mistake. A new hypothesis, however fruitful, is typically at least partially wrong. The account of a discovery is typically partly false.

Let us consider some cases of simple error. I add a column of figures and mistake a 4 for a 9. Each time I see the 4 I call it a 9, so that all my calculations are mistaken.

Suppose again that I meet a man walking along a beach. He looks to me like someone I went to school with and I begin to call him by name, remind him of former escapades, and tell him old jokes, but he turns out to be someone else.

In these examples I certainly treat one thing as another. In the second case there is a sense in which I treat the new as the old. But I do so in the manner of Epaminondas, reducing the new to the old, ignoring the differences until they are forced on me. This is again a way of avoiding the formation of a new concept.

Even if these examples are typical, however, error is significantly *related* to novelty. For one thing, the formation of new concepts typically leads to error. Every good new scientific theory is surrounded with error, as appears abundantly in retrospect. It is typical of insights that they are overstated. What is more, error often leads to the formation of new concepts.

This is not to say that the formation of new concepts can be understood as nothing more than making and correcting mistakes. It may seem to be so from the outside or in retrospect. Whenever disparate things are found to be similar—as in Newton's application of the laws of the mechanics of middle-sized objects to celestial bodies—it seems at first from the outside as though important differences are being ignored which must be taken account of later on. But this is only a partial view. It is not enough to say that new concepts come about through correcting the mistaken application of old ones. This leaves unexplained, as I mentioned in Chapter I, the source of the correction and the peculiar helpfulness of the error.

But it is common for a mistake to lead to novelty. It is as though we developed concepts for new situations only when we were frustrated in the attempt to subsume them under the old. When the man on the beach turns out not to be my old friend, I may begin to try to discover who he really is. When the nuclear particle turns out not to behave like any of those he is familiar with, the physicist may come up with the concept of a new kind of particle altogether. In this sense, error is fruitful for the formation of new concepts. The information uncovered in the attempt to subsume the new situation under the old concept may be the basis of the new concept. The juxtaposition of old concept and new situation involved in error may be precisely the sort of comparison required for establishing another kind of relation between old and new.

CONCEPT-INSTANCE

'This is a battleship.' 'Here we have a case of spotted fever.' 'This is sulphur.' All of these express the concept-instance relation. They are examples of what is commonly called the application of a concept to an instance, subsumption of an instance under a concept, or simply recognition or identification of a thing. Each of these phrases reflects a different way of looking at the process. 'Application', 'subsumption', 'recognition', 'identification', all single out special aspects of the function or form of the process.

In fact, unless we find a thing difficult to recognize, we are aware of no process at all. We simply recognize something; we see a battleship, we see that this is sulphur. But it is common, nevertheless, to speak of 'applying' concepts to things. And, in a sense, the application of a concept to an instance can be looked at as a way of treating the new in terms of the old. The concept is old, given, something to work with; and the thing is *this* thing, always new in the sense that it has never been seen before in all its here-and-now particularity.

This view breaks down, however, if we look carefully at the process of applying concepts to things. As we ordinarily think of them, concepts or ideas we 'have'; they are more general than things, and they 'fit' things more or less well. Our ordinary way of talking about concepts suggests that they are stencils with which we attempt to match the perceived world. The point about the concept-instance relation, so conceived, is that in the ordinary process of applying concepts to things no new concepts emerge. When we identify something as an instance of a concept already given we do nothing to modify our conceptual scheme; we simply order experienced things in terms of it. I can identify a cloud just passing over the horizon as nimbo-cumulus, or a fish I have just seen as a perch. But such things are not treated as new in any other sense than that I have not encountered them in all their particularity before. I act as though I had seen their type before. A girl says to a boy, 'I know your type', and she has him pegged. Her perception of him has changed, but not her category. In the ordinary application of concepts to things the concepts leave the process as they came in. Everything that is not old in the thing (not subsumable under the concept) is put aside. In this sense, the application of concepts to things is not a treatment of the new in terms of the old; it consists in sifting out of a potentially new situation something recognizably old.

The more dynamic way of looking at the concept-instance relation—the way advocated by Dewey and by the Gestalt psychologists and their followers—does not essentially change this. These writers point out the shortcomings of the stencil model of the concepts—instance relation. They point to the unity of structured situations (as opposed to 'concepts' and 'things'), to the sense in which 'applying the concept' is indistinguishable from perceiving the thing, to the role in such perception of active structuring on the part of the perceiver, and to the sense in which this always involves discovery. In the familiar Gestalt pictures, we can see how it involves activity and discovery to perceive antelopes, birds, bears climbing trees, old and young women, and the like. But, whether I see the figure as a bird or as an antelope, the concept in terms of which I see it is familiar to me. The discovery is that *this* can be structured in terms of such a familiar concept or Gestalt. It is significant that situations can be looked at in terms of more than one old concept, but this does not help us much in understanding the emergence of new concepts. A theory focused on the concept-instance relation finds it difficult to explain the new.

All of this applies, however, only to theories which treat concepts as corresponding to relatively fixed properties of things. In general we say that the concept of 'sulphur' applies to all and only those things that have the properties of sulphur—a certain place in the periodic table, for example. If we take away the stability of concepts, their relation to fixed properties shared by all and only members of the class, then the 'application of a concept' is less distinguishable from 'the formation of a new concept'. This is exactly what Wittgenstein (1953) with his notion of the 'family resemblances of things', begins to do. For him, there need be no set of properties shared by all instances of a term. We may recognize instances of the term only through an interrelation analogous to the overlapping similarities in appearance of members of a family. From this point of view, recognizing the 'next instance' of a concept may indeed require change in the concept itself. This unorthodox way of looking at the concept-instance relation will become clearer in terms of processes to be considered in the next section.

THE EXTENSION AND DISPLACEMENT OF CONCEPTS

In order to get at processes underlying the formation of new concepts, we have been considering ways in which the new is treated as the old. The difficulty with the processes considered, however, is that they require no *change* in concepts. Comparison, and the correct or incorrect application of a concept to an instance, have to do with the relation of concepts already formed, or the relation of concepts to situations stripped of their novelty.

But there are other ways of treating the new as the old.

Recently I learned to look at polishing as a process of making many tiny scratches. I had never thought of it this way before. I would probably have been willing to admit that a scratch is a scratch, irrespective of size, but I was not used to thinking of anything as a scratch that I could not see with the naked eye. (The irrelevance of size is not so apparent: the notion of a dry river bed as a scratch on the land is also a new one for me.) My notion of polishing changed, and my notion of scratching was made to include a new type of instance.

I know what a drum is. I know about snare, bongo, bass, and oil drums. But when I found myself in a metal room with a thin metal wall that reverberated whenever it was jarred, it was a new thought for me that the room was a kind of drum.

In these examples the concept of scratch or drum is not being 'applied'. The situations in question do not lend themselves to the ordinary use of these terms. I am not mistaking a room for a drum, or a polish for a scratch. Nor am I comparing 'room' and 'drum', except perhaps in the sense of somehow juxtaposing them.

What is most apparent here is that change of concept is involved. There is change in my concept of 'this' (polishing and the room), there is change in what I have been calling the concept itself (my notions of scratch and drum), and these changes are interdependent. The changes in my concepts of polishing and of the room are like the formation of new Gestalts of things, like the bird-antelope example. I come to structure these situations in terms of concepts new for the situations. But the changes in my concepts of scratch and drum involve something else. These concepts have been displaced to situations outside of their ordinary patterns of use and they have been transformed in the process. Through their displacement they have been extended. They have been made to include a new kind of instance.

'Extension' is an after-the-fact notion. It suggests that the concept has been made to hold or cover more than it did before. As I use it, it means more than that the concept's instances have been increased; it means that they now include a type of instance new for the ordinary use of the term.

'Displacement' is itself a metaphor for the process by which this extension is effected. It is a process of carrying over an old theory —here the notions of scratch and drum—to a new situation. The old theory comes to be seen in the new situation. The process is a way of treating the new as the old.

It is the main point of this chapter that the displacement of concepts is different in kind from comparison, error, or the application of concepts to instances; and that it is central in the formation of new concepts. Its uniqueness tends to be obscured, however, by our need to see processes of thought after-the-fact, in terms of their results. From this point of view, the example of polishing and microscratching can be seen as a case in which I recognize polishing as an instance of the general concept of scratching, here conceived in a way that makes 'scratch' independent of size. From the same point of view, I can be said to recognize that both the metal room and the drum are hollow containers over which a membrane has been stretched, producing noise when struck. But these notions—the size-independent notion of scratch and the notion of the membrane-covered, noise-producing container—came as a *result* of the processes I am discussing. I did not have them to begin with and therefore could not 'apply' them. To state otherwise is to read the result of the process back onto its beginning. This reading back masks the displacement of concepts and allows discovery to be seen in terms of the concept-instance relation alone—a fact which helps to explain why most writers on the thinking process have neglected the displacement of concepts.

The same tendency makes us limit the scope given to the

31

displacement of concepts, as indicated by the following cases:

(i) A child who has been used to calling 'drum' only snare drums played with a stick sees for the first time a small bongo drum struck with the hand, and recognizes it as a kind of drum.

(ii) I come to see the metal room as a kind of drum.

We tend to treat these as different kinds of processes, in which only the second involves a change in the concept of drum. But the child displaces and extends his notion of drum just as I do. The apparent difference is in the degree of familiarity to us of a concept of drum wide enough to include a bongo as opposed to one wide enough to include a room.

If a room as a drum is too familiar a notion, consider,

(iii) Coming to see as a kind of drum a man who keeps a meeting going by his regular, strong participation.

Every sign we give of having changed our concepts in (ii) and (iii), the child also gives. He begins to carry the term over to things he would not have applied it to before. He carries it over not merely to this particular bongo but to other things that share something of the bongo's similarities to and differences from the snare drum.

In this case, as is generally true with the displacement of concepts, extension of the concept to a new kind of instance requires a change in the concept that goes beyond its relation to that instance alone. A concept can be displaced in more than one way, yielding concepts bearing significant relations to one another. Consider again various ways in which 'drum' can be displaced and extended:

(i) a bongo as a drum
(ii) a room as a drum
(iii) a man driving a meeting as a drum
(iv) a peculiar-shaped rock as a drum.

Assuming that these processes begin with the same root concept—that is, the same starting point for displacement and extension—it is apparent that the same concept can be displaced and
extended in many different directions, yielding many different
new concepts. These may be more or less homogeneous. Each of
the concepts of 'drum' is broad enough to include the root case
(something similar to the snare drum). But they do not all include
the others. A snare drum is a drum in the sense in which a bongo
is; in the sense in which a room is; in the sense in which a man is;
and in the sense in which a rock is. In the sense in which a room is
a drum, a snare and a bongo are, too; but a man and a rock are not.
In the sense in which a man is a drum, the snare and the bongo are;
but not the room and the rock. The 'drum' concept according to
which a room is a drum, is homogeneous with the first two but
not with the last two. These drum concepts do not constitute a
class in the traditional sense of formal logic. They do not share a
set of properties that distinguish them from other things. Rather
they display the overlapping similarities Wittgenstein calls family
resemblance. Like children in a family, they can be seen to have
come from a common source, even though there may be no
unique feature or features shared by all. The family resemblance
of the different 'drums' is an effect of the concept's growth
through displacement.

So far, the formation of new concepts has been discussed from
the concept's point of view, but it can be discussed from the
world's point of view as well. In fact, the formation of new concepts is the other side of the discovery of the world.

It is true that not all discoveries involve the formation of a new
concept or a change in concept. I may discover (though it is
highly unlikely) that a certain protein contains an amino-acid it
was not known to contain before. My notion of the protein has
changed (I have a different concept of 'this') but my concept of
the amino-acid need not have changed. I have simply found a new
instance of the concept, not a new kind of instance. On the other
hand, when a child discovers that ice melts to form water, and
that water can be frozen to make ice, not only has he discovered

something new (for him) about the world, but his concept of 'water' has changed as well. His criteria have changed, and there has been an important change in the kind of instance to which he applies the concept. In the example of the room as a drum, I discover something about the way noise is made in a room. This discovery goes hand in hand with the displacement of the concept of 'drum' to the room. It is, in fact, another way of talking about it.

All formation of new concepts, all change in concepts, involves discovery of the world—that is, the development of a new way of looking at the world (reflected in statements about the way the world is) which may be more or less borne out as time goes on. Every theory of the formation of new concepts is also about discovering the way the world is.

This chapter has sketched a kind of process essential to the formation of new concepts: a way of treating the new as old, neither comparison, nor error, nor the application of concepts to instances, but a displacement of old concepts to new situations resulting in extension of the old.

I have aimed at a view of the formation of new concepts which neither denies them nor makes them mysterious. Its analogy to biology is most striking. Prior to the development and acceptance of evolutionary theory, the emergence of new biological forms was explained either by denying their novelty or by tracing them to essentially mysterious spontaneous generation. The function of the notion of the displacement of concepts is to approach an evolutionary theory of new conceptual forms.

CHAPTER III

Analogy and Metaphor

Before going further with the displacement of concepts, I will try
to relate it to 'analogy' and 'metaphor'—terms which might well
have been used in place of it. However, 'analogy' and 'metaphor'
are old terms and have a wide variety of partly related and partly
incompatible meanings, so that their use now is apt to be confusing. In this chapter some of their meanings will be sorted out,
related to the displacement of concepts, and selected for use in this
book.

METAPHOR

'Metaphor' has been used in two fundamentally different ways. In
the first and by far the most common sense 'metaphor' refers to a
part of language, so that a certain set of words may be said to *be*
a metaphor. This usage goes back at least as far as Aristotle:
'Metaphor consists in giving the things a name that belongs to
something else' (McKeon, ed., 1941, p. 1476). In this sense, 'The
world is my oyster', and 'That man is a lion' are metaphors.
In current parlance, 'oyster' and 'lion' are said to be 'vehicles' of
the metaphors, and their 'tenors' are said to be the messages con-
veyed about the man and the world. Sometimes 'metaphor' desig-
nates the vehicle itself, rather than the whole phrase.

This old sense of 'metaphor' is still very much alive. One of
the more recent instances of it is in *Words and Things* (1958) by
Roger Brown. Brown is primarily interested in the origin and

development of language, and he regards metaphor as one of the chief forms of what he calls 'semantic change'. The work of I. A. Richards has led him to be concerned with the difference between 'live' and 'dead' metaphors.

> The metaphor in a word lives when the word brings to mind more than a single reference and the several references are seen to have something in common. Sometime in the past someone or other noticed that the foot of a man bears the same relation to his body as does the base of a mountain to the whole mountain. He thought of extending the word *foot* to the mountain's base. The word *foot* then referred to two categories. These categories share a relational attribute which makes them one category. Within this superordinate category, which we might name the foundations or lower parts of things, are two subordinate categories—the man's foot and the mountain's base. These two remain distinct within the larger category because the members of each subordinate category share attributes that are not shared with the members of the other subordinate category. . . . Metaphor differs from other superordinate-subordinate relations in that the superordinate is not given a name of its own. Instead the name of one subordinate is extended to the other and this . . . has the effect of calling both references to mind with their differences as well as their similarities (Brown, 1958, p. 140).

> This metaphor blazed briefly for the person who created it and it lights up again when anyone hears it for the first time, but for most of us it is dead. This is because with repetition of the phrase *foot of the mountain* the word *foot* loses its exclusive connection with anatomy (ibid., p. 141).

It is interesting how this passage reveals Brown's static view of metaphor. For him a metaphor calls to mind two categories of reference and points to an attribute they share—here, 'the foundation or lower parts of things'. He sees metaphor as nothing more than a way of identifying two categories as subspecies of a common genus. The only difference is that in metaphor the genus, or

36

superordinate, 'is not given a name of its own'. But he does not see in metaphor the emergence of a new concept nor does he see that the concept or the superordinate may come into being only through the metaphor. This point of view is typical of many attempts to put metaphor into the rational framework of language and thought, where rationality is reduced to the concept-instance relation and the inclusion of categories.

There is another strain of theory in which metaphor is treated not as a piece of language but as a process of thought. This is Cassirer's 'radical metaphor':

> . . . transposition and substitution, which operate with previously known vocabulary as their material, must be clearly distinguished from that genuine 'radical metaphor' which as a condition of the very formulation of mythic as well as verbal utterance requires a transmutation of a certain cognitive or emotive experience into sound, i.e., into a medium that is foreign to the experience, and even quite disparate; just as the simplest mythical form can arise only by virtue of a transformation which removes a certain impression from the realm of the ordinary, the everyday and profane, and lifts it to the level of the 'holy', the sphere of the mythico-religious 'significance'. This involves not merely a transference . . . it is not only a transition to another category, but actually the creation of the category itself (Cassirer, 1946, pp. 87–88).

My 'displacement of concepts' is essentially Cassirer's 'radical metaphor'. Cassirer is clear about metaphor's role in the emergence of new concepts, but his concern with it is primarily in mythic, poetic, and religious rather than scientific and common-sense modes of thought.

ANALOGY

Analogy is also broadly ambiguous. It may refer to a relationship, signified by a phrase, or to a process of thought.

The former is again the more common. Writers tend to look at

37

analogy as a special sort of relation. The point becomes clear when we look at two treatments of analogy by writers who differ in cultural background, historical setting, discipline, and reason for dealing with the subject.

For Hoffding, in his *Le Concept d'analogie*, analogy is:

> . . . a similarity of relations between two objects, a similarity which is not based on particular properties or parts of these objects but on reciprocal relations between these properties or parts (Hoffding, 1931, p. 7).

He finds analogy in the relation between already formed concepts. Analogy may be 'used' to discover new hypotheses, but it is not in itself involved in the formation of new concepts. It is of interest primarily because there are certain categories which can be related only by analogy, for example, psychology and epistemology, and because analogies express 'religious or poetic states' which recall the unconscious life of the soul.

As far as its role in scientific discovery is concerned, Hoffding believes that analogy is a way of getting to a new hypothesis. Once the hypothesis has been formulated and 'exact premises' have been made, the analogy can be discarded. The very fact that he speaks of the 'use' of an analogy suggests that for Hoffding the similarity of relations is already there, already conceptualized, at the time it functions in the formation of a new hypothesis. Oddly enough, he does identify another kind of process in which 'a part is grasped as symbol of a whole', where the common elements that justify the process do not emerge until later. But he believes that these 'primitive or involuntary analogies' are characteristic only of primitive men. He does not see in them a pervasive aspect of 'civilized' human thought as well.

Polya, in *How to Solve it*, deals with analogy only as a technique for mathematical problem solving. But he treats it in an identical way.

> Analogy is a sort of similarity. Similar objects agree with each other in some respect, analogous objects agree in certain relations of their respective parts.

A rectangular parallelogram is analogous to a rectangular parallelepiped. In fact, the relations between the sides of the parallelogram are similar to those between the faces of the parallelepiped: Each side of the parallelogram is parallel to just one other side, and is perpendicular to the remaining sides. Each face of the parallelepiped is parallel to just one other face, and is perpendicular to the remaining faces. Let us agree to call a side a 'bounding element' of the parallelogram and a face a 'bounding element' of the parallelepiped. Then, we may contract the two foregoing statements into one that applies equally to both figures: Each bounding element is parallel to just one other bounding element and is perpendicular to the remaining bounding elements.

Thus, we have expressed certain relations which are common to the two systems of objects we compared, sides of the rectangle and faces of the rectangular parallelepiped. The analogy of these systems consists in this community of relations (Polya, 1945, p. 37).

In short, analogy is a similarity of relations between concepts, categories, or objects; it is what Brown called the 'common attribute' between the parts of a metaphor. What Polya, like Brown, does not discuss or appear to recognize is that the concept of the shared relations—in this case the relation of 'bounding elements'—is one that emerged from the very process he calls 'use of analogy'. If the common concept was not at first 'there' to be 'used', in what sense was the analogy there to be used? Can you 'use' an unconceptualized similarity?

Finally Oppenheimer, in 'Analogy in Science', treats analogy as

. . . a special kind of similarity, which is the similarity of structure, the similarity of form, a similarity of constellation between two sets of structures, two sets of particulars, that are manifestly very different but have structural parallels.

Like Polya and Hoffding, he recognizes that analogy has something to do with the discovery of new hypotheses. But like these writers, he thinks that what is involved is the 'use' of analogy, i.e.

39

the use of a similarity of relations which has already been conceptualized. Analogy does not in itself involve the formation of a new concept; it comes rather from an observation of similarity in concepts already formed. Oppenheimer departs from this somewhat in his theory of the *correction* of analogy, which has been discussed and criticized in Chapter I.

Essentially all three writers regard the use of analogy as consisting in subsumption of two or more concepts, categories, or objects under a more general concept or category which has already been formed. Oddly enough, their examples sometimes belie this usage. They are not really examples of the use of a general concept at all. Examples following their formulation rather than their experience would probably strike them as unintelligent or uninteresting—just because they involve nothing new.

There is another kind of usage, according to which 'analogy' means 'argument by analogy'. Here a process of thought is involved but it is generally conceived as a process of evaluation or justification of a proposition already formed. If I wish to prove that Jones is intelligent, I argue Smith is intelligent and Jones is in most other ways like Smith. The form of the argument is: since x and y share attributes a, b, c, they share d as well. While logicians have criticized argument by analogy because of its obvious susceptibility to error, they have also sometimes claimed that argument by analogy is essential to induction. Most recently, N. R. Hanson (1958) has tried to show the relevance of argument by analogy in justifying the proposal, though not the acceptance, of scientific hypotheses.

ANALOGY AND METAPHOR IN THIS BOOK

The foregoing gives the main lines of usage of these terms, but it is by no means exhaustive as an analysis. Its purpose is to suggest the relation of these terms, as ordinarily used, to what I have called the displacement of concepts.

The term metaphor I will use in its traditional, narrow sense to mean 'giving a thing a name that belongs to something else'.

I will say that phrases like 'the mountain's foot', 'screening ideas', 'going up in the world', *are* metaphors. Metaphors, in this sense, are the traces left by the displacement of concepts. They bear witness to complex processes of displacement of concepts over time just as present living species bear witness to biological evolution.

I will also use 'analogy' in its traditional sense to mean a similarity of relations between concepts or objects. The displacement of concepts does not consist in the observation of such a similarity, since at the time of the displacement these shared relations have not been conceived. But the displacement begins with the intimation of such a similarity and may be justified after the fact by pointing out the similarity in terms which are themselves results of displacement. Observation of analogies is the result and partial justification of the displacement of concepts.

HISTORY OF ATTITUDES TOWARDS METAPHOR AND ANALOGY

Why has so little attention been paid to the role of metaphor and analogy in the formation of new concepts? I have been making some sweeping statements about their function in a way that sounds, at times, obvious. If their function is so obvious, why have writers on the subject made so little of it?

This question directs us to the history of theories of metaphor and analogy. Here we find two main schools of thought, one developing partly in reaction to the other, and both furnished with excellent reasons for ignoring the innovative role of metaphor and analogy.

The first school of thought, which I will call rationalist, goes back again to Aristotle's *Poetics*. Aristotle presents metaphor as one of many rhetorical devices whose function is to serve as an ornament to language.

The perfection of diction is for it to be at once clear and not mean. The clearest indeed is that made up of the ordinary

41

words for things, but it is mean. . . . On the other hand, the diction becomes distinguished and non-prosaic by the use of unfamiliar terms, i.e., strange words, metaphors, lengthened forms, and everything that deviates from the ordinary modes of speech. . . . These, the strange word, the metaphor, the ornamental equivalent, etc., will save the language from seeming mean and prosaic while the ordinary words in it will secure the requisite clearness (McKeon, ed., 1941, p. 1478).

This is the doctrine of metaphor as window-dressing for language. It goes hand in hand with the assumption that there is available as an alternative a clear non-metaphorical way of speaking whose function is to convey meaning.

This way of thinking beautifully suited the rationalist temper of the eighteenth century, committed as it was to the view that things are inherently intelligible and that theories, if they are based on reason, can convey that intelligibility by the use of clear language made up of 'the ordinary words'. Why, except for ornament, should anyone choose to talk about 'the chariot of Phoebus' when he could as well talk about the sun? Hobbes foreshadows this view in *Leviathan*:

The sixth [cause of absurd conclusions] is the use of metaphors, tropes and other rhetorical figures, instead of words proper. For though it be lawful to say, for example, in common speech, 'the way goeth, or leadeth hither, or thither:' 'the proverb says this or that,' whereas ways cannot go, nor proverbs speak; yet in reckoning, and seeking truth, such speeches are not to be admitted (E. A. Burtt, ed., 1939, p. 146).

We find these ideas taken up by Locke and by other philosophers of the Enlightenment. Metaphor and analogy and other 'figures of speech' seemed to them confused and obscure, a part of the darkness of mind in which the immediately preceding centuries appeared to them to live. To admit to metaphor and analogy a central role in human thought, in scientific discovery, would be to let chaos in the back door.

This habit of disbelieving in the functional role of analogy and metaphor was (as C. S. Lewis has said of the habit of disbelieving in demons) a kind of protective device: it permitted the philosophers of the Enlightenment to pay no attention to the metaphors underlying their own thought where, as we will see and as many have pointed out, they have the run of the house.

The attitude of Aristotle and of the Enlightenment has persisted in our own tine. It is with rhetoric and English literature that we ordinarily associate metaphor and analogy. We place them in the province of poets and critics. We generally give them no place in rational argument or in scientific thought. Sholom Aleichem, in *Bunche Schweig*, makes God say to the defending angel, 'No metaphor!' From this rationalist point of view, we are not free to look at the role of metaphor in the formation of concepts, in the discovery of hypotheses; to do so would erode the base of rationalism itself.

Throughout the growth of the rationalist viewpoint, there has been an a-rationalist reaction. This conflict has come to a head during the last two centuries over scientific method. Scientists and philosophers of science, bearers of the rationalist tradition, have fought for 'clear and distinct language' as opposed to the obscurity of metaphor and analogy embodied in myth, religion, poetry, literature. Positivists began in the early years of the twentieth century to call metaphor 'merely emotive', devoid of cognitive meaning.

One effect of the rationalist onslaught was to force the opposition into an equally extreme position. Thus there has been much defence of metaphor, in poetry and myth, as a kind of truth separate from and better than the truths of science. The defenders have claimed what have been variously called 'presentational', 'symbolic', 'metaphoric', or 'mythic' truths. These they have wanted to make completely separate, and therefore safe from the truths of science. For Suzanne Langer, for example, there are two essentially separate modes of symbolism, 'discursive' and 'presentational'. The former is the mode of science; the latter the mode of art, myth, music. The two modes are not reducible to

43

one another and are equally valid, in their separate domains, as routes to understanding. Langer, as a disciple of Cassirer, is not unaware of the fact that metaphor has something to do with the formation of new concepts (presumably of new concepts in what she calls 'discursive thought'), but the primary drive of her *Philosophy in a New Key* (1957) appears to be to establish the existence and validity of certain kinds of truth quite apart from the demands of scientific method.

Once again there is a reason not to look intensely at the role of metaphor in the formation of new concepts in ordinary life and in science: it would tend to endanger the carefully built distinction between scientific and symbolic truths.

In short, the conflict between partisans of scientific and metaphoric truth, with pressure for the dominance of one or for complete separation of the two, has kept us from recognizing and examining the role of displacement of concepts in discovery, and in the formation of concepts generally.

THE ROLE OF METAPHOR IN LANGUAGE

But this conflict has not prevented the development of a number of theories of the role of metaphor in *language*. Somehow it has been possible for many writers to notice the dominant role of metaphor in language without carry-over to the formation of concepts.

It has become a truism that language is full of metaphor. From their various points of view, Wegener, Cassirer, Langer, I. A. Richards, Erich Fromm, and Roger Brown, among others, have asserted it at length. Still, this often-repeated fact never ceases to shock, when it is taken seriously—that is, when we examine one by one the metaphors of which our speaking and writing are made.

Am I going *up* in the world or *down*?
How do I feel? *Warm, cold, bitter, tender, acid, hard, irritated, wounded, refreshed, excited, dark, bright*?

What kind of man is he?—*upright, downcast, noble, grasping, tight, dull, sharp?*
What kind of day is it?—*cheerful, threatening, gloomy, sad?*
How *long* have you been working?
Where does the river *run?*
If you are *in business,* are you a *driver,* a *sparking plug,* a *self-starter,* a *cog in the machine?* Do you *fit in?*
During the last year, did you *make a hit, play on the team, play to win, slug it out, strike out, reach a stalemate?* Are you *on the ball?*
Did you know the *big man,* the *little man,* the *chiefs,* and *Indians?*
Did you *sell* a friend on going to the movies? Did you *make a deal* with him to go?

All of the italicized words (and perhaps some that are not) are used metaphorically; that is, they make their familiar referent a symbol for the new situations to which they refer.

Focusing attention on the metaphors in ordinary language is like focusing on the colour green. We see it everywhere. It has, too, the effect of immediately removing the film of obviousness that covers our way of looking at the world. If 'fitting into' an organization is a metaphor, what is the nature of the process for which it is a metaphor? If 'seeing' the meaning of a sentence is a metaphor, and so is 'understanding', then what are understanding and seeing about? Metaphors give us, in one way, our sense of the obvious. We do not understand 'seeing' any better than we understand 'understanding', but it is obvious that in order to understand, we need *clarity, definition, simplicity, distinction.* These words are part of the displacement of our theory of seeing to understanding. They are 'obvious' just for that reason.

The claim that 'language is metaphorical' is no small claim. It has the most serious implications for our notions of thinking and of the world, and the relation of our thinking to the world. But the metaphorical claim has been made in various ways and with varying degrees of seriousness. Three forms of this claim will be examined briefly here, not to prove or disprove them but to uncover some of their consequences.

The Radical Function

Metaphor is a Principle of Growth in Language

In her *Philosophy in a New Key* Suzanne Langer quotes Phillip Wegener as follows:

> In a genuine metaphor, an image of the literal meaning is our symbol for the figurative meaning, the thing that has no name of its own. . . . But if a metaphor is used very often, we learn to accept the word in its metaphorical context as though it had a literal meaning there. . . . The great extent and frequency of its metaphorical services have made us aware of the basic concept by virtue of which it can function as a symbol in so many contexts; constant figurative use has generalized its sense.
>
> All words, therefore, which may be logically subjects (of prediction) and hence expository . . . have acquired the capacity only by virtue of their 'fading' in predicational use. And before language had any faded words to denote logical subjects, it could not render a situation by any other means than a demonstrative indication of it in present experience. So the process of fading which we have here adduced represents the bridge from the first (one-word) . . . phase of language to the developed phase of a discursive exposition (Langer, 1957, pp. 140–141).

Langer then adopts Wegener's view as her own:

> The use of metaphor can hardly be called a conscious device. It is the power whereby language, even with a small vocabulary, manages to embrace a multimillion things; whereby new words are born and merely analogical meanings become stereotyped into literal definitions. . . .
>
> Speech becomes increasingly discursive, practical, prosaic, until human beings can actually believe that it was invented as a utility and was later embellished with metaphors for the sake of a cultural product called poetry (ibid., p. 141).

More recently, Roger Brown, in his *Words and Things*, identifies metaphor as one of the two basic forms of semantic change. I have quoted him at length in Chapter III.

46

These writers see metaphor as a process of generalizing change in language. New literal language is made by the emergence and then the dying or fading of living metaphors.

But Brown's view of metaphor is more static than Langer's. He treats metaphor as the application of the same name to different categories of reference which share one or more properties. He is able to do this only by reading back onto the origin of the metaphor the 'superordinate category' which emerged through the process of metaphor itself. Therefore, the problem of the relation between the metaphorical word and its referent, which led Langer to her notion of 'presentational symbolism', does not exist for him. He finds in it merely a special case of the relation between genera and species.

Metaphor is a Primitive Form of Language

The theory of metaphor as a process of linguistic growth is related but not identical to the theory of metaphor as a primitive form from which, over the centuries, our current quasi-literal language has developed. It is one thing to look at the process of metaphor as a recurrent feature of the growth of language and another to believe in a metaphorical era—like the Jurassic era—in the history of the development of language. Erich Fromm, in *The Forgotten Language*, proposes such a theory.

While Fromm uses the phrase 'symbolic language', his 'universal symbolism' is substantially a kind of metaphor, as I have been using that term.

> The universal symbol is the only one in which the relationship between the symbol and that which is symbolized is not coincidental but intrinsic. It is rooted in the experience of the affinity between an emotion or thought, on the one hand, and a sensory experience, on the other. . . . The universal symbol is rooted in the properties of our body, our senses, and our mind, which are common to all men and therefore, not restricted to individuals or to specific groups. *Indeed, the language of the universal*

47

> *symbol is the one common tongue developed by the human race, a*
> *language which it forgot before it succeeded in developing a universal*
> *conventional language* (Fromm, 1951, pp. 17–18).

According to Fromm, dreams, myths, and fairy tales are residues
of this earlier forgotten language, from which literal, discursive
language has grown up to form a rather thin top layer. He does
not make a very serious attempt to justify this historical claim,
but illustrates the related symbolic character and content of
dreams, myths and fairy tales. In various ways his theme is a version of earlier writings by Jung and Malinowski. This view represented in its time a break with the old, rationalist view of the
temporal and logical priority of literal language.

All Language is Metaphorical

Neither Wegener, Langer, Brown, nor Fromm takes a clear-cut
position on the question of the metaphorical character of all
language. To say that language grows metaphorically, or that
metaphor is a more primitive state of language, or that metaphor
is 'ubiquitous', is not the same as saying that *all* language is metaphorical—that is, that the symbolic relation is the principal and
exclusive relation involved in linguistic reference.

Langer has a revealing example in this connection. She con-
siders the word 'run':

> If we say: 'the brook runs swiftly,' the word 'runs' does not
> connote any leg-action, but a shallow rippling flow. If we say
> that a rumor runs through the town, we think neither of leg-
> action nor of ripples; or if a fence is said to run around the barn-
> yard there is not even a connotation of changing place. Ori-
> ginally these were probably all metaphors but one (though it
> is hard to say which was the primitive literal sense). Now we
> take the word itself to mean *that which all its applications have in*
> *common, namely describing a course* (Langer, ibid., p. 140).

But what about this phrase, 'describing a course'? Is it, in its con-
48

text, a piece of literal or metaphorical language? What is the literal sense of 'describe'? Does it contain reference to the use of language? If so, can a fence be said to describe a course in any but a metaphorical sense? And the word 'course'—doesn't it mean, literally, a route that is walked or run? And doesn't this make 'course of a fence' a metaphor?

It can be objected that I am here confusing 'literal' with 'etymological' meaning. But this simply underlines the difficulty of determining the literal meaning of a word. What *are* the literal meanings of 'describe' and 'course'? Can we spell them out in terms whose 'literal' status is *not* dubious?

The difficulty of identifying literal language, if such exercises are taken seriously, has led some writers, among them I. A. Richards, to wonder whether, with the possible exception of formal systems, literal language is not a will o' the wisp. In formal systems like mathematics and symbolic logic, it is possible in theory to relate terms to one another by rules of substitution without any reference to referents. In these systems, a term's 'meaning' is exhaustively defined by the rules of substitution that apply to it. Here there may be no need to bring up the notion of metaphor. (Even here, generalization within the system must be explained, and so must the transformation the system undergoes when an attempt is made to apply it to the 'real world'.) But elsewhere, Richards has suggested, in all use of language in relation to the world, there is nothing but metaphor, no relation but the symbolic relation between words and the things they mean.

If hardly anyone has adopted this extreme version of the metaphorical view, it is perhaps because of its disturbing consequences. Some of these consequences have to do with the nature of meaning. The symbolic relation is vague and mysterious. We can never come to an end of spelling it out; it admits of an indefinite number of possible specifications. If it is taken to be the principal relation between terms and their referents, then we lose the notion of 'single meaning' and with it the canons of clarity on which much current philosophy is based. Instead, vagueness and ambiguity become the rule, the 'natural' state from which the artificial clarity of formal systems is a deviation.

This view has consequences, as well, for the familiar conflict between 'conventional' and 'natural' theories of meaning. There may be intrinsic appropriateness or inappropriateness in a metaphor; and if the usual relationship between terms and their referents is metaphorical, then there may be appropriateness or inappropriateness in this relationship as well. It is *as if* terms had natural meanings. It is not a matter of indifference whether we say 'His temper flared up' or 'His temper fizzled up', and it is cavalier and inconsistent to say simply, 'This is what I will mean by "fizzled".' If naming is not labelling but the displacement of concepts, then naming is subject to understanding and to criticism. This suggests a new, more acceptable basis for the theory of 'natural meaning'.

Perhaps the most troublesome consequences, however, are for theories of truth. Common sense, and much of contemporary philosophy, would like to say that a statement is true if and only if it asserts what is the case. But this assumes a univocal, literal relationship between the statement and some state of affairs; that is, a single literal-meaning theory for statements as well as for words. But a metaphor cannot be 'true' in this way. All metaphors are in one sense false, in fact absurd. It is absurd in one usual sense of 'runs' to say that a fence runs around the house. In the sense in which the statement is not absurd, it may be believable. But in this sense it is also far from univocal. Metaphors are subject, with equal appropriateness, to an indefinite number of interpretations. Assuming that each of these interpretations could be given literally, the statement may have an indefinite number of senses in which it may be true, and an indefinite number in which it may be false. However, on the theory we are now examining, each interpretative statement would itself be metaphorical and hence not simply resolvable in truth or falsity. In short, if there are no literal statements, there is no literal truth.

It can be objected that if most or all of our statements are metaphors, still they have truth or falsity of a kind—that is, some characteristic by virtue of which we commit ourselves to them or not—and we seem to do pretty well, for the most part, with this metaphorical truth or falsity, whatever it is. The problem is not so much a problem of ordinary practice, however, as it is a problem for theories of truth, philosophies, intellectual ideals, theories of education, and the like. Granted some kind of truth or falsity in ordinary practice, if we cannot understand it in terms of what we have been trying to define as literal truth, how can we understand it?

In the last few pages, we have reviewed some of the current theories of metaphor and language: that metaphor is a principle of growth in language, that it is a primitive state of language, and that all language is metaphorical. The last theory is most significant for the displacement of concepts. Without attempting to come to a conclusion about it, it is clear that the great difficulty in identifying literal language and in reducing metaphorical to literal language raises serious questions about it and therefore about its consequences.

It remains to relate these assertions about metaphor and language to the displacement of concepts and to the question of the scope of that process. What I have been calling the displacement of concepts is simply another word for the process of metaphor, in Cassirer's sense. Specific metaphors (pieces of language) are results and signs of that process.

For reasons mentioned in the previous section, metaphor has not usually been discussed in the context of concept formation. But language is the repository of our concepts. To speak of the growth of language is another way of speaking about the formation of concepts. The metaphorical character of language (whether merely 'ubiquitous' or universal) is due to the fact that our language, at any given time, gives us a cross-section of our processes of concept formation or discovery. The metaphors in language are to be explained as signs of concepts at various stages of displacement, just as fossils are to be explained as signs of living things in various stages of evolution. There is no more sense in opposing metaphorical and discursive truths than in opposing earlier and later stages in the life of the same species or organisms. The ubiquitousness or universality of metaphor in language can be explained by the ubiquitousness or universality of the displacement of concepts in concept formation.

CHAPTER IV

A Close Look at the Displacement of Concepts

INTRODUCTION

So far I have posed the problem of the emergence of new concepts, and suggested that new concepts come through the shift of old concepts to new situations. In this process the old concept is not applied to the new situation, as a concept to an instance, but is taken as a symbol or metaphor for the new situation. The new concept grows out of the making, elaboration and correction of the metaphor. There is no one point at which it emerges since the process is continuous, like the emergence of a biological species, and its freezing at any one point is always arbitrary.

When we look more closely at this process, which has been discussed so far in a monolithic way, a number of phases can be distinguished. I will single out four of these under the headings of transposition, interpretation, correction, and spelling out. These are not discrete events following one another in a fixed order but aspects of the process often out of sequence and often inseparable. In this chapter I will discuss these phases and the scope of the process as a whole, its variations in duration and character and its relation to other kinds of experience. Consideration of the symbolic relation will focus attention on the nature of the relation between old concept and new situation; the basis of the selection of old concepts for displacement; and the way in which new hypotheses come out of the displacement of concepts. Finally I

53

will examine the relation of these questions to the possibility of a logic of discovery, the emotional undercurrents of discovery, and the scope of the displacement of concepts.

A Schema for the Displacement of Concepts

Let us go back to the example of the 'cold war', a concept whose cycle of emergence and development has taken place largely within our own time. Walter Lippmann is supposed to have been the first to use the term in connection with the international situation. His doing so was an example of what I want to call the *transposition* of an old concept to a new situation, that is, the making of the metaphor. It is the first shift of old concept to new situation, the first establishment of a symbolic relation between old and new. I use 'displacement', on the other hand, to refer not only to this initial shift but to the full working out of the process of metaphor.

The process of transposition is complicated by the fact that there are in ordinary thought and discourse no isolated concepts, but only concept clusters or, in an informal sense, theories. The concept of 'war' involves a cluster of concepts like 'enemy', 'battle', 'army', 'declaration', 'truce', 'winning', 'loss', 'gain', 'advance', 'retreat', 'casualty', 'outpost', and the like. We could never be sure the list of these related concepts was complete. We could not even say, except in the context of a specific inquiry, which of these concepts was the 'central' one. The boundaries and the internal structure of the concept are changing and indistinct.

The phase of transposition, therefore, is not a once-and-for-all affair. It goes on indefinitely as more and more concepts from the old concept cluster are shifted to the new situation. This is part of the elaboration of the metaphor. Thus, Americans have come to speak of Russia as 'our enemy' in the cold war and of England as 'our ally'. Americans speak of cold war 'skirmishes', such as Korea and the Congo; of 'defeats', as in Cuba; it is debated whether there is a state of 'stalemate' or of slow Russian 'victory'. With each passing month the concept fills out.

In these examples, 'transposition' is inseparable from *interpretation*, the assignment of a concept from the old cluster to a specific aspect of the new situation. The enemy is Russia, the ally—England, the defeat—Cuba, and so on. Transposition and interpretation ordinarily occur in a single gesture. We do not transpose an old concept to a new situation without transposing it to some specific aspect of the new situation. But the two phases are still distinguishable, as evidenced by the fact that we are sometimes aware of wondering what aspect of the new situation an old concept *is* assignable to, or even whether it is assignable to anything at all. Was the cold war ever 'declared'? What are the 'weapons' used in it?

When the displacement of a cluster of concepts has begun, a potential for transposition and interpretation has been set up. It is as though all concepts in the old cluster wanted to be carried over and located in the new situation.

The process of transposition and interpretation does not proceed with perfect freedom. The new situation has a conceptual structure of sorts before any old theory is displaced to it. We had ways of looking at the international situation before Lippmann's 'cold war'—we spoke of post-war 'adjustment', of Russian 'greed for power', of the gradual establishment of peace. This preexisting structure resists some transposition and interpretation, and there is resulting adjustment in the process of displacement. This I call *correction*. The process is not a one-way affair in which the old theory is corrected to suit the new situation, as would be suggested by the model of the old concept as a kind of stencil fit over the new situation. It is more like mutual adaptation, in which the old theory and the new concept-structured situation are modified in various ways so as to suit one another. With the development of the concept of a cold war, our notion of war has changed as well as our notion of the international situation.

This mutual adaptation takes a variety of forms. Aspects of the old theory may be rejected for transposition to the new situation—as when we question whether the cold war was ever 'declared'—and they may in the process cease to be necessary to our notion of the old theory as well. Old concepts may be compounded, as in this case 'cold' and 'war', in order to become more appropriate to the new situation. The interpretation given aspects of the old concept may be changed—as when we come to treat propaganda and financial aid, in addition to arms, as 'weapons' of the cold war. We may limit the areas of the new situation to which the old theory may be transposed—as we would do, for example, if we exempted our affairs with Canada from the field of the cold war.

This process may be a conscious critique of displacement of the old theory or it may be a series of implicit adjustments, such as we make in walking over rough ground.

In this way the metaphor is elaborated. We come to understand what concepts from the old cluster are to be transposed to the new situation, what their interpretation is, what area of the new situation they are limited to. In the process, their reference to the new situation becomes more familiar and conventional. We become less and less aware of using old terms in a figurative sense, with a reference back to the old theory, and more and more aware of two equally legitimate senses of the same term. Already we use 'cold war' without much conscious reference to 'war' in any other sense. This is what I. A. Richards calls the 'dying' of the metaphor, which we can see here as an integral part of the displacement of concepts.

When the attempt is made to work out the relation between these senses—the areas of community and difference between the old and the transposed theory—I say that the metaphor is being *spelled out*. This requires a more explicit attempt at formal theorizing than is common in ordinary practical inquiry. Roger Brown gives an example of it, in the passage quoted in Chapter II, when he says that the foot (of a mountain) and the foot (of a man) have in common the property of being the base or foundation of things. But this metaphor is so old as almost to have lost its metaphorical character altogether. I am not aware that anyone has attempted to spell out the sense of 'cold war' as it refers to the present international situation. An attempt could be made along the following lines:

> To say that we are engaged in a cold war is to say that we are engaged in an international conflict, in which we are one of a set of parties hostile to one another, determined to attain exclusive control of territories and peoples. To this end, we employ a variety of means, short of total military aggression.

This is inadequate and incomplete, but typical of the spelling out even of those metaphors we have come to use with ease. The process of spelling out is always incomplete, at least in the sense in which transposition is, since every transposed concept requires its own spelling out and the transposition is never complete. Moreover, the spelling out itself is apt to be metaphorical, as in Brown's use of 'foundation' and my use of 'conflict' and 'control'. This raises problems for the ordinary distinction between literal and metaphorical language similar to those discussed in Chapter III. If we must use metaphor to spell out metaphor, then we never come to the literal bed-rock. At best, the literal-metaphorical distinction is a distinction in function; for a given metaphor, the literal language is similarly what is used to spell it out.

Transposition, interpretation, correction, and spelling out represent abstract phases in the displacement of concepts, but these phases always occur in a specific context from which the source of energy comes. It may be primarily speculative and playful, as when a child is amused at the idea of a boiling tea-kettle as a baby crying, or a biologist is intrigued with the notion of heredity as the transmission of coded information. On the other hand, the process may be stimulated by the problem of understanding or action, and may be part of an attempt to cope with the problem. The development of our notion of the cold war has been part of our attempt to understand and cope with the international situation. The displacement of wave theory has been part of our attempt to understand and control the behaviour of light. In the problematic context, the displacement of concepts provides the basis for the development of new hypotheses, new ideas for solving the problem.

In by far the greater number of cases, however, the displacement of concepts in speculative or problematic contexts is not deliberate. We find ourselves confronted with partial displacements, as part of the culture's gift to us, transmitted through the language, and, for the most part unaware, we pursue them.

THE SYMBOLIC RELATION

According to the generalized schema given above, new concepts are formed through elaboration and correction of theories displaced from old situations to new ones. The distinction between this displacement and the literal application of concepts to instances has been made to hang on the fact that in the displacement of concepts the old theory is symbolic of the new situation. But the nature of the symbolic relation so far remains obscure.

Unfortunately, there is not much in the literature to help us on this point. While a great deal has been written about the symbolic relation, most of the writing has been done by philosophers and, among these, chiefly by philosophers of art. For reasons explained in the last three chapters, there has been far more attention to the role of symbol and metaphor in art, religion, mythology, than in science and common sense. A traditional explanation of the symbolic relation has grown up according to which x is a symbol for y when x and y have a similarity of relations, that is, a relation of analogy, as Hoffding, Langer, and others have used that term. But this view is wholly inadequate for our purposes.

When we treat the symbolic relation as a similarity of relations, we bring through the back door the old denial of mystification of novelty. For the symbolic relation, as we are concerned with it, holds between old theory and new situation *before* elaboration of the metaphor. At this point what relations are similar? If they can be stated, we are, by definition, after the fact—that is, after the elaboration of the metaphor; for a statement of these shared relations is precisely a spelling out of the metaphor. If they cannot be stated, what does it mean to call the symbolic relation a similarity of relations? This would be to read back onto the beginning of the process what can emerge only at the end.

In the light of this, the symbolic relation is perhaps better understood as the *intimation* of a similarity of relations. When I first become aware of the room as a kind of drum, I have a dim perception—warning, preconscious sensing—of a set of shared relations which will become explicit only later on. This intimation would be the basis, then, for the symbolic relation between my notions of drum and room. The idea of 'symbolic relation' would acquire reference to a perceiver and to a special kind of perception.

For one thing, it presents the familiar and the unfamiliar, the old theory and the new situation, as equal partners in the relation. But in the formation of new concepts the symbolic relation is not symmetrical. The new is seen in the manner of the old. Aspects of the room are seen as related in a drum-like way. It is true that my notion of drum changes as it is displaced. Nevertheless, the room is perceived in the manner of a drum, not the reverse, and this is reflected in the metaphor.

But this, too, is unsatisfactory. Intimation is a word for feelings. It has a touch of mystery in it. It requires feeling that something is the case before you can justify it. But what is felt? Merely that you will be able to say afterward how the room is drum-like? There is another function involved. With the intimation of the symbolic relation, the old theory is taken as a *programme* for exploring the new situation. Here it is helpful to remember that a concept in use is theory-laden. It can be spelled out in an indefinite series of expectations to the effect that this would happen, if that is the thing it is thought to be, and such-and-such were done.

If this is a drum, then, when it is struck, it will make a noise.
> the harder it is struck, the louder the noise.
> it will have a membrane which will spring back when you push against it.
> and so on.

59

A word like 'drum' signifies such a series of expectations. When we make a metaphor like 'The room is a kind of drum', we can carry over each of these expectations in a symbolic way. Armed with the concept, we can spin off expectations indefinitely, each of them providing a new basis for exploring the new situation. 'We are in a cold war with Russia' indicates a programme for exploring our relations with Russia, much as $'x = 2y$, where $y = 1, 2, 3, 4, 5 \ldots'$ gives a programme for exploring the value of x.

The analogy to equations suggests another aspect of the function of an intimation that $'x$ is y-like'. Given $'x = 2y'$ we need not remember all the values of x for values of y. We can generate them from the formula. The formula is a condensed version of these pairs of values. Similarly from a symbolic relation, once established, an indefinite number of possible related aspects of the new situation can be generated and considered. Metaphors are easily carried and can be made to generate indefinite series of expectations which need not be remembered since they can be generated again. They have the condensation essential to instruments of thought.

Still more primitively, even at the point of intimation metaphors are ways of *naming* aspects of the new situation and therefore fixing and controlling them. This function should not be underestimated. In every displacement of an old theory to a new situation there is a feeling of transition from helplessness to power. Before, we were aware only of what was puzzling and disturbing; now, suddenly, there is something like clarity and a basis for action.

'This man is a little Hitler.'
'Luther King is another Gandhi.'
'The south is going through another Reconstruction.'
'Russia is in the throes of religious conversion.'

These metaphors, however appropriate or inappropriate they may be, name, fix, and structure what might otherwise be vaguely troubling situations. Armed with them we feel the ability to generate hypotheses, expectations, policies. Without them, we are merely confused. They are our way of learning from the past without being tied to it.

This function is never more apparent than in our attempts to make a deliberate change. We cannot change unless we can conceive what we might be, however dimly, if we were not what we are. But this requires a new concept of our self (our self-image, as psychologists refer to it) and it is true of new concepts of the self, as of new concepts generally, that they emerge from old ones. James Joyce in *A Portrait of the Artist as a Young Man* speaks of discovering that he must 'forge the conscience of his race in the smithy of his soul'. Franklin Roosevelt helped to develop the concept of America as 'the good neighbour'. Christ said to the fisherman that henceforth he would be a 'fisher of men'. The very establishment of a symbolic relation provides a focus for change and a programme for the exploration of change, where change was not concretely thinkable before.

The symbolic relation, then, requires intimation that a new situation has aspects related in the manner of an old. This, in turn, means taking an old theory as a programme of symbolic exploration of the new. The old theory becomes in this function a set of condensed expectations, a way of naming and fixing the new, a proto-concept, a basis for change. But this symbolic carrying-over of old expectations remains obscure.

It may be useful, however, to compare it with the literal application of a concept to an instance. A concept extends into a series of expectations. When we apply the concept to an instance, we bring these expectations to bear on the situation where they are either met or not met, so that the concept is found applicable or not. In contrast to this, there is in the displacement of concepts a peculiar vagueness. The displaced concept is used to structure the new situation (I see the room as a drum as I see the animal nibbling the begonias as a rabbit), but its appropriateness to the new situation is unclear. Most of all of the expectations associated with it will not be met as we are used to having them met. It is unclear what expectations are to be carried over and how they are to be met or not. Rather, the old theory seems to act in the new situation as a vague model.

Consider as an example the metaphor implicit in 'learning to play a role in an organization'. In this phrase, the concept of role-learning is carried over from our ideas of drama and play-acting. In an organization, many of the expectations connected with role-learning would not be met: there is no writing of roles and no memorizing of them (job descriptions in some companies excepted), but there is in organizations a process which is to organizational roles what memorization is to a role in a play. And so 'role' and 'role-learning' can be used for these aspects of organizational life.

Here the theory of role-learning is a specific which can serve as a model in a number of ways. The particular ways in which it is to serve as a model come clear only with actual juxtaposition of the old and the new. The old term then comes to indicate related aspects perceived in the new situation which cannot yet be stated in any other way. The process works backwards for the old theory, too, since it comes to be seen in terms of its character as a model for the new situation.

More formally,

1. Everything, and every expectation involved in the concept of a thing, can be structured in an indefinite number of ways. We can never be sure of having grasped them all.
2. How the thing is structured depends on what it is juxtaposed with.
3. When an old theory is symbolically transposed to a new situation, it is juxtaposed with it in the manner of a projective model. We are asked to find aspects of the new situation related in the manner of the old. 'Find the old x in the new y'.
4. Through such a juxtaposition we are able to find in the new situation aspects related in the manner of the old, which we had not previously seen in the old.

Every metaphor, then, is an implicit riddle. It says: find the old in the new. Like all riddles, it is projective. There are an indefinite number of ways in which the old can be found in the new. The ways chosen are in part the contribution of the perceiver. To illustrate, consider the following. Here *B* is a kind of *A*; find *A* in *B*:

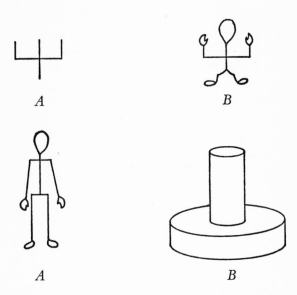

These examples are simple projective tests. *A* is to be found in *B*, and *A* is found in *B*. An effect is to change the way *B* is perceived. In the first example, *B* comes to be perceived as an outgrowth of ⊔. In the second, the column comes to be seen as *resting* on the base. But in both examples we come to see *A* in a new way, too. We see ⊔ as the schema of a man, rather than of a pitchfork or a candelabrum; and we see ⋔ as something standing on a base. We have to see *A* in a new way in order to see *A* in *B*; and the new way of seeing *A* comes out of our finding *A* in *B*.

In these examples, there is little novelty. *A* and *B* are about equally familiar and there is nothing very new for us about the way we come to see either one. But in the displacement of concepts a relatively familiar *A* is taken as a projective model for a

63

novel and puzzling B. As a result A is found in B, but an A seen as it had never been seen before.

We can say, then, that an old theory, A, is in a symbolic relation to a new situation, B, when:

1. There is an intimation that B is A-like.
2. A is taken as a condensed programme for exploration of B.
3. In carrying out this programme, expectations from A are transposed to B as projective models.
4. For each of these projective models, aspects of B are seen to be related in A-like ways, where we had not been attentive to those relations in A before.

This can be distinguished now from application of a concept to a familiar kind of instance.

In the application of a concept A to an instance B, A is found in B with no resulting change in the way in which A is perceived.

Compare seeing the animal in the begonias as a rabbit with seeing a river bed as a scratch in the land. In both cases a familiar notion is found in a present situation; it functions as a projective model for the present situation. But only in the second does that functioning require the familiar notion to change.

This explanation gives off only enough light to reveal a new problem: through what process do we find a way of seeing A in B which gives a new way of seeing A as well? This is a problem but not a mystery. We have at least the elements of a possible explanation. The new is to come from the old (not from nothing). And the old theory becomes new as it changes to meet the demands placed on it as a projective model for restructuring the new situation.

THE SELECTION OF CONCEPTS FOR DISPLACEMENT

We have dealt at some length with the symbolic relation, but have not so far asked why one concept rather than another comes to be in a symbolic relation to a given situation. This question quickly turns into two. When we are confronted with a new situation, why does one metaphor rather than another come to mind? And on what basis, of those that come to mind, is one or more selected for a special role?

It is, of course, no answer to say that 'drum' comes to mind in connection with the room because the room is like a drum. We can see after-the-fact that it is like a drum and like other things as well. The question is why, of the many things it could come to be seen as like, *this* one comes to mind and is singled out. The question suggests answers in several directions. One has to do with what is available in the culture; another, with the function of metaphors in theories; and a third, with the relation of metaphors to the demands of a situation. All these factors influence the selection of metaphors. Without directly answering the question of appropriateness in the selection of metaphors, they suggest some things about it.

Our culture provides the materials from which our metaphors are made. Our technology, our social system, and, in the informal sense of the term, our theories of the world, provide us with concepts for displacement. They are our 'given'. When we come to form theories of business organization, we derive our metaphors from the games we know, from the church and the army as we know them, from our understanding of machines. Our psychologies are based in part on the physics of a few generations ago. Our science takes its metaphors from concepts current in the same or related disciplines, even from common sense. Our slang is a patchwork of cultural gifts. Only in American culture could people talk and think about 'blasting off' a new project, 'touching all the bases' in getting a project approved, 'changing gears' in carrying through a plan, 'moving into outer space' in developing ideas, taking a 'blue-collar attitude', making an organization of 'chiefs and Indians', undertaking a 'crash programme', and the like. All of this is in the nature of a truism. If our metaphors did not come from the culture, where else would they come from? These conceptual resources can be seen as gifts or ties. The culture

65

gives us concepts we could not do without, but leaves us no choice.

In many cases the culture takes a more active role. Current language provides us with metaphors whose elaboration has already begun. Metaphors current in the culture impose themselves in our very efforts to seek words for new and puzzling situations. They have a kind of priority so that in many areas we cannot think without being influenced by them.

In the domain of education, we are confronted by phrases like 'intellectual growth', 'academic fare', 'taking a course', subjects 'hard or easy to digest'. These all suggest the metaphor of education as nutrition. When someone suggests a 'balanced educational programme' he is probably making a still further transposition from the theory of nutrition.

In our ordinary talk about leadership, we use phrases like 'guide', 'direct', 'go first', 'explore'. We talk about 'pitfalls' and 'guiding people around them'. Apparently our ways of thinking about leadership are displaced from theories of travel, passage, or directed movement from one place to another. The very word 'leader' seems to have been a metaphor based on leading (going first) in movement from one place to another. Relatively new theories of 'directive' and 'non-directive' leadership are further transpositions of this same metaphor.

We talk about people 'going up' or 'going down' in the world, about social 'scales', 'ladders', 'hierarchies'; 'social climbers', 'rising and falling stars'; people of 'high' and 'low' position; 'upper' and 'lower' classes. Our language reflects our view of our social system as an up-and-down affair that can be climbed or descended. Our jokes build on it, playing on a mixture of appropriate and inappropriate transpositions, as when it is said that 'the higher a man climbs on the ladder of success, the more we can see of his lower regions'. 'The Lower Depths' and 'Room at the Top' are further transpositions. We have to search for words for a society in which, for a given position, there would be no one below and above.

In these few examples, concepts already in process of displacement, as reflected in the language that comes to us 'naturally', seem to force us, often unaware, to deal with new situations by making still further transpositions from the old theory. It is useful in this connection to look at metaphors as having lives of their own. They propel themselves through the culture, seeking elaboration and expansion. They operate best when we are unaware of them, invading area after area of thought. So it is with the metaphor of the machine, the family, Christianity, business, to name a very new.

But 'culture', as I have been using it so far, is vastly over-simplified. We belong to many cultures, concentric and over-lapping. I participate in the cultures of humanity, the Western World, the United States, American industry, the particular company I work for—to begin what could be an indefinitely long enumeration. Each of these cultures offers characteristic theories, ways of thinking, for displacement to new situations. In a sense, I carry with me a personal culture, made up of ways of thinking and acting that are characteristic of, and perhaps idiosyncratic to me. These are reflected in my language, and they are fruitful as sources of metaphor. Notions drawn from games, music, Jewish culture, academic life, business, product development, sales, in various combinations, occur to me for displacement. I carry with me certain crucial events and relationships which serve as projective models for future situations. Just as Americans can see in a man 'another Roosevelt', I can find him 'another Fred' (a teacher and friend of mine). A new task can appear to me as a kind of Hotel Griswold— a place I worked when I was seventeen. My past, which is not quite anyone else's although it shares in every-one else's, provides me regularly with concepts for displacement to new situations, and these have for me a certain priority. This storehouse of potential metaphors is a major part of my person-ality.

The theories of our various cultures with their various priorities, as reflected in our language, supply us with, and sometimes impose on us, the theories from which our metaphors are made.

But the gifts of the culture are virtually infinite, and while many are called few are chosen. Something must be said about the selective role of the situation itself.

The displacement of concepts is apt to occur in a difficult, puzzling, new, confused, or obstructed situation—what John Dewey calls a problematic situation; or in a playful, speculative, 'what would happen if . . .' kind of situation in which there is nothing problematic to begin with, although out of playful speculation a problematic situation may arise. We are used to thinking of the situations we are in as passive with respect to us, waiting for something to be done to them. But typically we perceive them as making demands on us; they will not let us alone.

We build a staircase that does not want to sit quite stable; we are caught in the dilemma of our relations with Soviet Russia, where no approach, however belligerent or ingratiating, promises clear sailing; we are asked to work in an organization where some people concentrate on establishing their own status and security at the expense of their tasks. It is as though these situations asked to be cleared up, explained, straightened out.

Metaphors that come to mind and are selected result from the interaction of what is given or imposed by the culture with the demands of the situations confronting us. Theories are chosen from among the culture's store, on the basis of their ability to meet these demands—to give rise to metaphors which will explain these troubling situations or allow them to be changed. In this sense, the metaphor of genetic material as coded information has been selected for its use in genetics; in psychology metaphors of 'conformity and deviance' and 'stamping in' have been useful in explaining and predicting behaviour; the metaphor of medicine, with its notions of diagnosis, treatment, cure, has been the basis on which psychiatry has been able to grow; the metaphor of the machine, for all its defects, has been a primary basis for the growth of industrial organizations.

But in the displacement of concepts a familiar theory is carried over as a projective model for a new situation. The structure, the clearing-up, emerges only as the metaphor is elaborated. At the time the metaphor comes to mind and is first selected, its likely effect on the situation cannot be stated explicitly. Therefore, examples of 'useful' or 'fruitful' metaphors, like the ones above, are inevitably after-the-fact. We can to some extent decide whether to continue to use them on the basis of their effect in the situation, but this evidence is not available to us at the time of their first selection. How, then, do we select them?

I am thrown back again on the notion of intimation. In the establishment of a symbolic relation, there is an intimation that aspects of *B* are related in the manner of *A*, which means functionally that *A* is taken as a projective model for exploration of *B*. In a problematic situation, when *A* is taken in this way, there is an intimation that *B* will be clarified as it is treated in terms of *A*. If I look at the staircase as a series of beams . . . If I look at the situation with Russia in terms of our World War II conflict with Germany . . . If I look at the organization as a kind of royal court . . . I have the feeling that it will become clear what needs to be done. This is perhaps nothing more than saying 'I have a feeling that the new *B* turns out to be similar in partial ways to the *A* with which I am familiar.'

Intimations of this kind are usually accompanied by feeling-clues. The metaphor is apt to seem peculiarly satisfying, intriguing, beautiful or simply to have a kind of 'pull' about it. There is often a feeling of increased vitality. The aesthetic or simply hedonic quality of certain ideas for solving problems has occasionally been remarked, though without specific reference to metaphor. Feelings of this kind act as signs, pulling us along a path of solution, even though choice of that path cannot be justified at the time.

If metaphors fruitful of useful solutions and explanations are first identified through such feelings more often than would be expected on the basis of chance alone, then reference must be made to some kind of pre-knowing, to a dim or preconscious anticipation of the results of elaboration. This seems to have some relation to what is experienced, but it presents difficulties. If what is sensed as an intimation of the fruitfulness of a metaphor corresponds to what is preconsciously anticipated about the elaboration of that metaphor, then an enormous amount of preconscious work is presupposed. Metaphors must be selected and screened in a preliminary way for their likely effect in the situation. But the selection of the metaphors to be screened at this point can have no relation to the way the metaphor will actually perform in the situation; otherwise, *this* anticipation would have to be accounted for, presumably by another layer of intimation. So that something very much like a random trial and screening process would seem to be involved. Other writers, notably Poincaré in his 'molecular' theory of ideation, have been willing to presuppose such a process together with the enormous informational capacity it implies.

On the other hand, it is tempting to think of explanations that avoid such presuppositions. Perhaps intimations are self-fulfilling as they apply to the selection of metaphors. From this point of view, one metaphor may be potentially as useful as another, the problem being to generate enough energy to pursue one, undertaking the full work of elaboration and restructuring. The feelings attached to the metaphor, here totally unrelated to anticipation of its usefulness, would be the means of generating this energy. It would be no wonder then that the metaphor characterized by this feeling turns out to be useful; it would simply be the one that has been fully tried.

There is appeal in this view since it avoids much that is difficult to explain. And it is true that any theory can serve as a projective model for a new situation. But the presupposition of this view—that no metaphor, initially, is any more appropriate to a situation than any other—implies an epistemological relativism that is also difficult to swallow. Certainly different metaphors lead to different theories, and it is a matter of experience that theories vary in their usefulness. Even if some weight is granted to self-fulfilling intimation, a good deal of dim anticipation is still left to be accounted for, presumably along lines similar to those outlined above.

These considerations are aimed at explaining how metaphors are brought to mind and selected as appropriate to the demands of situations. But there is more to selection than appropriateness.

Concepts often come to be displaced to situations out of erroneous attempts to apply them. We think we have an X, only to discover that it is a 'kind of X', 'something on the model of an X'. The history of science is full of such examples. (I believe these are actual processes underlying Oppenheimer's notion of discovery through misapplication and correction of an old hypothesis.) Cases in point are development of the wave theory of light from wave theories of liquids and sound, and development of theories of atomic structure from earlier attempts to apply to atoms theories of the structure of the solar system. Nineteenth-century mechanism began by approaching physiology with the view that bodily processes could be seen as instances of mechanical ones, but as time went on mechanism came to function more as projective model than as applied theory.

This kind of movement of thought is characteristic of many processes of discovery. Error functions as a guide to discovery. Misapplication of a theory, based on a partial misapprehension of what is in the situation, guides us to the use of the theory as a projective model for the situation. Children thrive on a similar process. They call a croquet mallet a bat; they proceed to discover, through a variety of experiences, how it is not a bat; but in the meantime their notion of a bat, and of games in which a bat is used, serves for them as a projective model for playing croquet. The transition from erroneous application of the *old theory* to its displacement is part of what gives continuity to their learning. And, since their first identification of the situation is never wholly erroneous, the error assures them of some appropriateness in their choice of metaphor.

Metaphors also come to be selected out of the fact that new situations are never wholly without a conceptual structure. Any situation for which we attempt to develop new theories already has theory-structure of a sort. So there is a tendency to select metaphors which are already implicit in the language of the theory, or which mesh in certain ways with the metaphors underlying the theory.

Organic chemists like to talk about carbon-hydrogen linkages, double bonds, long chain molecules, and the like. It is not much of a leap for them to think about cross-linkages and side-chains. These notions could be considered further elaborations of the central metaphor of mechanical linkage. But organic chemists are generally less comfortable with anthropomorphic metaphors (atoms that like to combine with some but not other, families of atoms, atoms that need something) or with architectural metaphors (atomic domes, windows, joists, and the like). In the face of a new or puzzling situation in organic chemistry, the organic chemist is subject to a strong current tending to displace notions from the field of mechanics.

When metaphors are selected to mesh with other metaphors already embodied in the theory they sometimes cover up problems which would be embarrassing otherwise. In the eighteenth and nineteenth centuries, for example, the difficulty of sustaining the mind-matter dualism came to a head over the problem of explaining the will. Explaining the will required explaining how an extensionless mind could possibly act on an extended body. Mechanical theories, displaced to the mind, offered an apparent solution. When 'making up your mind' is treated as a matter of adjusting mental 'forces', choosing the 'weightier' of two arguments, yielding to the 'stronger inclination', and so on, we have the illusion of a continuous series of mechanical forces acting on one another. Instead of the problem of mind acting on body, we have the illusion of one body acting on another. Those who used the mechanical metaphor would deny the *literally* mechanical view of the mind, but their selection of the mechanical metaphor saved them the problem of the will. Such functions are powerful motives in the choice of metaphor.

In brief, then, at least three factors influence the coming to mind and the selection of theories for displacement:

1. the theory-resources of the various cultures to which we belong, with all their overlapping priorities, given and sometimes imposed by our language, including

2. the metaphors already underlying our theories of the new situation; there is a tendency for the new metaphor to mesh with these, and

3. the demands of the situation itself 'asking' to be straightened out in certain ways.

The new metaphor emerges out of the interaction of the cultural gifts with the demands of the situation and expresses itself in intimations of significant similarity, i.e. in intimations that the displacement will be effective in resolving the problematic situation. Such intimations can be seen as reflecting processes of pre-conscious screening and elaboration and also as having a self-fulfilling character, since the metaphors pursued are only those which have been intimated. A similar process is involved when the metaphor emerges out of the erroneous attempt to *apply* an old theory, the problem shifting here to the selection of the theory for application.

These comments are incomplete in at least two ways. With respect to the actual determination of metaphors for selection, they only touch on the personal feelingful function of the metaphor and its problem-solving function in the situation. This interplay seems to me to be of the first importance. It is as if a theory came to be selected for displacement to a given situation only if it provided satisfaction on both levels. Second, these comments have largely avoided the question of the appropriateness of a theory for displacement—the question which seems to me to go back to the epistemological questions raised in Chapter III.

NEW IDEAS FROM THE DISPLACEMENT OF CONCEPTS

One of the factors governing the selection of metaphors in a new situation is the metaphor's effectiveness in leading to 'new ideas'. I do not mean a new concept, in the sense of a new theory, but the segment of a new theory that functions as a potential solution to a problem of action or explanation in a given situation. In this sense, it is a new idea that plastic can be foamed if gas is formed while it cures; that magnetic tape can be made to contain more information if the iron oxide particles stand on end; that smog may be due to a temperature inversion; that allergies may be psychogenic, and so on. 'Idea' in this sense is roughly equivalent to 'hypothesis'.

This section will be concerned with the emergence of new ideas from the displacement of concepts. Rather than embark at once on a theory of the process, I will begin with a series of examples from which, later on, some inferences will be drawn.

The first of these examples refer to cases of new product development in which I have been a participant or an observer.

At a meeting of product development chemists and a theoretically oriented physical chemist, a problem was raised about nylon and natural-bristle paint brushes. The nylon brushes had a tendency to deliver paint in fits and starts rather than in the smooth, continuous way of natural-bristle brushes. A number of changes in the nylon brush had been tried, including tapering of the bristles, flagging the ends (to approximate to natural bristles), the use of finer bristle, and the like, but all without success. The problem was to account for this difference in the behaviour of the two kinds of brushes, and then to devise some way of improving the nylon brush.

The group began by trying to understand what happens when paint flows through a brush. The physical chemist attempted a rough and ready model of the process. In a brush, he said, paint flows through 'pipes', that is through channels formed by the fibres of the brush. Just as liquid can be pumped through a pipe, so paint can be pumped through the channels of the brush. The pumping action in this case is due to downward pressure and release as the brush is drawn across the painted surface.

The product development man who had been working with the brush recalled at this point that the natural bristle brush shows a smooth curve when it is pressed against a surface, whereas the nylon brush tends to bend at a sharp angle. It then occurred to several at once that the gradual curve of brush fibres might tend

74

to provide a uniform, gradual pumping action, with continuous flow of paint through the brush, but that a sharp bend would tend to force all the paint out suddenly, and that this would account to some extent for the observed behaviour of both kinds of brushes.

We were concerned, then, to find some way of making the nylon bristles bend in a smooth curve. Our first thought was to reinforce the bristles at the point where they bent sharply and perhaps to weaken them elsewhere. We thought about splitting them differentially—that is, splitting the fibres at different heights and making sure that split fibre predominated except at the point where the angular bend tended to occur. In this way we hoped to even out the bend of the brush.

This was dismissed as impractical: it would be too expensive, and besides it was not clear how you could get most unsplit fibres at the bending point and most split ones elsewhere. But we felt this was something like what we would want to do. The question became: how can we get something like the effect of splitting fibres without splitting them?

It was pointed out that the effect of splitting the fibres differentially could perhaps be achieved by bonding them differentially. By making more bonds at the bending point, you could even out the bend.

One of the product development men had the idea then that this could be accomplished if a thermosetting adhesive could be dusted onto the brush and heat-set differentially.

This example raises a number of issues. It provides a little prototype of the way in which cross-disciplinary groups can function usefully together. The physical chemist gave a theoretical

75

model of the process, albeit of a 'plumbing physics' kind. The product men took up the model and related it to the observed

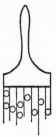

behaviour of the brushes. They related the physical chemists' theory about a way to meet the goal to a practical way of doing it.

More significantly here, the example illustrates in two ways the emergence of new hypotheses from the displacement of concepts. The behaviour of the brush came to be understood in the first place by displacement of a theory of the flow of liquid through pipes. The fibre channels were not really pipes, the flow of paint was not flow in the same sense, the 'pumping' was not pumping in the same sense—but the notions of channels, flow, pumping, gave a metaphor in terms of which the behaviour of the brush could be understood. This metaphor arose as theories from one discipline were carried over to another.

Secondly, after the goal of obtaining a smooth bending curve in the nylon brush had been set, the notion of differentially splitting the bristles served as a projective model for the notion of differentially bonding them. The second approach came in answer to the question, 'How can the bristles have the effect of being differentially split without actual splitting?'

Some members of our product group were concerned with the design of a new cleaning device, and began by attempting to understand some cleaning devices with which we were familiar. Some of the devices considered were vacuum cleaners, a mop and pail of water, a broom and sawdust, a rotary street sweeper. In all of these cases it seemed that cleaning involved the following steps: loosening the dirt from the surface to which it was attached, transferring the dirt to an *environment* more easily transported than the dirt itself, and then transfer of dirt-in-environment to a storage place. The nature of this environment varied according to the device. It could be air, water, or even sawdust. As long as the dirt was sparser in the transporting environment than it was on the surface being cleaned, the cleaning process could continue. It continued until the concentration of dirt in the two environments came into something like equilibrium, and then redepositing of the dirt began. To prevent this from happening, a fresh environment had to be provided from time to time.

Out of this came the idea of providing a closed environment which would be self-refreshing. The actual device deposited cleaning liquid on an enclosed surface and sucked up dirty liquid, which it then filtered and redeposited.

Here again, the theory of the situation to be explained grew out of the displacement of concepts from another area of discipline (one in which 'environment' was at home) and the actual solution came in response to the metaphor of a 'closed, self-refreshing environment'. It should be noted that this idea could have come from a number of other sources as well. After it had been developed, it was clear enough that some existing devices employed a similar system and that the new device could be understood as a modification of these existing ones. Characteristically, a new theory or an invention, after it has been made, can be seen to be derivable from other theories and things as well. This is not to say that other theories and devices would have been equally useful and evocative as a starting point for the idea. Our concern here is with metaphors functioning for an individual in process of discovery. What enables a metaphor to function in this way for an individual has to do with its relation to his personal culture, its emotional meaning for him, and the sort of feeling-clues accompanying it.

Our product group was presented with the problem of devising new wire-based fastening methods, superior to nails in some applications, so as to increase markets for wire. In this case a number of metaphors were involved and their interaction was complex, a situation in some ways more characteristic than the last two examples.

We had been intrigued for some time with the (perhaps legendary) theory that winds of hurricane force can blow a straw into a tree. One group member, Paul Matisse, had been intrigued enough to design a fastener on the model of it, an air gun that blew a wire brush into wood, causing the wires to broom out in the wood and providing considerable holding strength. We had been interested in some experiments showing that liquids, such as liquid adhesives, could be injected into solid surfaces and, building on this, we had talked about the possibility of a wire-injector. Finally, another man in our group, Charles Laws, had been fascinated with the idea that a pin could be driven through a penny, if it were given enough columnar support to keep it from buckling.

We were intrigued, then, with a wire-fastening device which would in some way take off from the phenomena of a high-velocity blow gun, a hypodermic needle, and the pin-through-the penny.

Laws designed a device which provided a support hole for fine wire, and used a plunger to push the wire through the hole into wood, the wood fibres then taking over the supporting function of the support hole.

Rough notions of intriguing phenomena were used as projective models for a fastening device. The phenomena themselves were interrelated. The pin-through-the-penny, for example, could be seen as providing by columnar support a rigidity high velocity wind gave to the straw! After the fact, the central notion seems to have been that a fine fibre could be inserted into a fibrous material like wood with relatively little force, if ways could be found to keep it from buckling. But this is more like a spelling out of the driving metaphors, after the invention has been made, than a description of the metaphors that led to invention.

In all of these product examples, the 'idea', the new hypothesis, is much more a beginning than an end. In each of the cases mentioned, the hypothesis which appears here as a solution, growing out of metaphor, was in fact the beginning of a long and difficult development project, whose difficulty and length would be surprising to anyone who had not participated in development work. Metaphors operated in these instances to yield fruitful hypotheses which, in turn, permitted development work to begin. They did not take the place of this work.

In these examples, an invention was the matter of primary interest. Theory of an informal kind entered as a route to invention. Theoretical questions—how does paint flow in a brush? what is cleaning? why will a pin go through a penny when it is given columnar support?—played a crucial role in permitting the emergence of a fruitful metaphor, but these were by no means the primary goals. The role of the displacement of concepts is equally important, however, in processes where the making of new theories is the dominant aim.

For one thing, scientific language is full of sleeping metaphors, the residue of earlier displacements of theories from other areas of discipline. Consider phrases like 'biological transducer', 'atomic wind', 'genetic code', 'electromagnetic wave', 'radioactive decay', 'chemical linkage', 'electrical reservoir', 'computer memory', 'voltage drop', 'sound absorption'. Scientific writings are full of such phrases, indicating carrying-over of concepts, as projective models, from one discipline to another.

It is always possible, of course, that such metaphors reflect ways of explaining or teaching theories rather than the genesis of the theories themselves. In Chapter V, I will try to counter this view with internal evidence taken from various theories. But we also have a kind of external evidence in accounts of the development of theories from metaphors by those who participated in their development. Some such accounts are available, as in the case of the theory of the discovery of the benzene ring, the notion of the brain as a kind of central telephone exchange, and the like. In fact, there has been an increasing body of writings devoted to the role of 'analogy' in scientific theory. Such writings suffer, to my mind, from wrong constructions put on the process of metaphor—

79

typically, by a downgrading of its importance, an attempt to regard it as something ancillary to scientific method proper rather than as an essential process in the emergence of new scientific concepts. But this is not always the case. In *The Philosophy of Science*, Stephen Toulmin gives an account of the development of concepts of light in which metaphor plays a more central role, although he himself views metaphor as a simple 'extension' of concepts without concerning himself very much with the difference between metaphor and the ordinary application of concepts to instances.

Toulmin takes as an example the discovery that 'light travels in straight lines', a discovery which was as revolutionary at one time as it now appears commonplace.

> ... the optical discovery is, in part at any rate, the discovery that one can speak at all profitably of something as travelling in these circumstances, and find a use for inferences and questions suggested by this way of talking about optical phenomena—the very idea that one should talk about anything as travelling in such circumstances being the real novelty.
> ... in the optical case, both the key words in our conclusion—'light' and 'travelling'—are given new uses in the very statement of the discovery. ... Until the discovery, changes in light and shade, as we ordinarily use the words ... remain things primitive, unexplained, to be accepted for what they are. After the discovery, we see them all as the effects of something, which we also speak of in a new sense as 'light', travelling from the sun or lamp to the illuminating objects. ... It is worth emphasizing ... how far by accepting [the physicist's way of looking at optical phenomena] we are required to extend the notions of light and travelling ... it would be somewhat queer, in the sort of situations with which the physicist is concerned, to talk in the ordinary sense of the word of anything 'travelling' at all ... the introduction of the notion of 'light' as something 'travelling' is not the simple, literal discovery of something moving, like the detection of frogs in a flower bed ... it is an extension of the

notion of travelling to do a new job in the service of physics (Toulmin, 1960, pp. 20–22).

In my terms, the discovery of light as something travelling is a metaphor, the elaboration of 'travel' as a projective model for light, so as to permit formulation of hypotheses which explain problematic material. The subsequent development of the theory of light can be seen, in part, as elaboration and correction of the metaphor.

> ... although only some of the questions which ordinarily apply to things which ... travel do so in the extended use, one cannot say beforehand which questions will and will not apply, and it has to be discovered as time goes on how far the old questions can be given a meaning in the new type of context (ibid., p. 38).

Toulmin goes on to show how the metaphor of light 'travelling' is elaborated in theories of refraction, and then how discoveries in physical optics required still further revision of this concept of 'travel'.

The account of the process given here has the difficulty of being at some distance from the actual process of discovery. I find it more difficult to give first-hand examples of the role of displacement of concepts in the generation of new scientific theories than in cases of product development and invention. However, there is another class of examples in which the displacement of concepts seems to me to come out clearly. I have explored the use of metaphor in forming notions of simple geometrical figures, and subsequently in solving such problems as the finding of area and volume. Thanks to my own scanty knowledge of geometry, these examples have provided me with first-hand and rather conscious examples of the role of metaphor in the formation of theories new to me, and suggest an intriguing teaching approach as well.

This area of exploration was suggested by an example given in Wertheimer's *Productive Thinking*, although Wertheimer interprets it in terms of 'insight' instead of the displacement of concepts.

He gives the problem of finding the area of a parallelogram. Rather than beginning in the usual way with the formula (*ab*, where *a* is the altitude and *b* the base) he starts with a rectangle

(1)

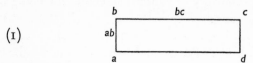

and makes the student discover the basis for the formula of the area of the rectangle, *abcd*

(2)

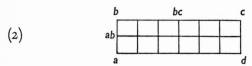

in the fact that there are as many unit rectangles in the figure as there are units in *ab* times units in *bc*. Then he presents the parallelogram.

(3)

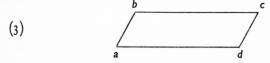

He induces the student to see the parallelogram as a 'distorted rectangle', that is, a figure which could be made into a rectangle by lopping off an 'excess' triangle from one end and placing it in a triangular 'hole' in the other.

(4)

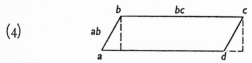

A ring of paper in the shape of a parallelogram is a way of stimulating this discovery.

(5)

Then the student can see that, since the parallelogram is equivalent to the area of a rectangle *abcd*, its area will also equal *abcd*, and he can see that the *ab* of his remade rectangle is equivalent to the altitude of the parallelogram.

What Wertheimer has done, I would say—what enables the student to achieve what he calls 'insight'—is to induce the student to take the rectangle as a projective model for the parallelogram, to see the rectangle in the parallelogram. When he has done so, his way of seeing the rectangle changes as well. If the rectangle can become this,

(6)

it can also become this,

(7)

approaching as a limiting case, this,

(8)

The rectangle now appears as the mid-point of an infinite series of figures of this form:

(9)

Wertheimer then illustrates, in the problem of finding the area of the following figure,

(10)

how this way of finding the solution to the parallelogram problem can function, itself, as a metaphor. After the student has seen the parallelogram as a distorted rectangle, he may be able to see figure (10) as one-half of figure (11)

(11)

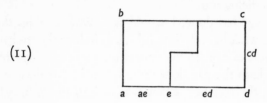

whose area is $\frac{1}{2}ab \times (ac + ed)$. In this sequence, the problem generated is one of finding the

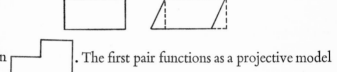

series in  . The first pair functions as a projective model for finding in the second what I would describe, from this after-the-fact viewpoint, as a regular, familiar figure of which the present irregular unfamiliar one can be seen as a determinate part.

This example led me to explore the problem of finding the formula for the volume of a sphere. I began, analogously, by attempting to understand the formula for the area of a circle, πr^2. Translating π as perimeter/diameter, this formula resulted:

(1) $$A = P \cdot \frac{r}{2}$$

This seemed to say that there are as many $\frac{r}{2}$-s in the area of the circle as there are units in the perimeter. This suggested in turn that the area of the circle is what is swept by a full 360° rotation of a radius, just as the face of a clock is what is swept by one of its hands.

(2)

Why $\frac{r}{2}$ then, since this analysis would seem to make the area of the circle the sum of as many radii as there are units in the perimeter? The radius has no area, however, but is only the limit of a figure having area. And this figure with a single generating point in the centre, but as many terminating points as there are units in the perimeter, must be a triangle. The area of that limit of a triangle will be base (1 unit of perimeter) times height (r) over 2. So that $A = P.\frac{r}{2}$ can be taken as saying that the area of the circle consists of as many such radius-triangles as there are units of perimeter.

I came to understand the area of a circle, then, in terms of the metaphor of a figure swept by the limit of another figure. This may seem to be a long way round. It is certainly no way of proving that the formula is correct, but only a way of discovering it if you had not grasped it before. However, it enabled me to find the formula for the volume of a sphere, which I had not known before.

How could I come to see the volume of a sphere in the manner of the area of a circle? The volume of a sphere is also what is swept by something—it is what is swept by the limit of a slice or wedge whose base is a diameter of the sphere.

(3)

The volume of the sphere will be made up of as many such wedges as there are units in the sphere's perimeter.

We can take a similar approach to the area of a triangle,

(1)

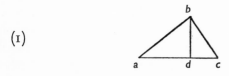

Its formula is $\frac{1}{2}ac \times bd$. The triangle can be seen as a stack of lines, in this way,

(2)

There will be a line between base and apex whose length will be $\frac{1}{2}b$; the rectangle $a . \frac{1}{2}b$ will be equal in area to the triangle. Again, this may seem to be the long way round, but it provides an intuitive (that is, metaphorical) way of understanding the area of a triangle. It also leads to the volume of a cone.

For when we ask how a cone can be understood in the manner of the triangle, above, we see in the cone a stack of circles.

(3)

There will be a circle between base and apex, whose area is one-third the area of the base circle, and the cone will be equal in volume to a cylinder whose height is the height of the cone and whose cross-section is equal in area to this circle.

(4)

Examples such as these, crude as they are, illustrate the displacement of concepts in the formation of new, informal theories.

Incidentally, they offer an approach to teaching geometry, among other subjects. This would involve ordering the materials of a course so that what had just been learned, in the sense of forming a metaphor-based theory about it, could serve in turn as a metaphor for the next situation that had to be dealt with. The student would be encouraged to see in the new situation a version of the problem he had just learned to solve.

In all of these examples the new hypotheses arise out of partial elaboration of the metaphors in question. They are all transpositions and interpretations of aspects of the theory that is being displaced. And, as in the case of the working-out of any symbolic relation, they represent the results of projection of aspects of the old theory in the new situation. Differential bonding of fibres, in the paint brush, comes of seeing the brush in terms of differentially split fibres. The cleaning tool comes of attempting to see in a cleaning device a closed and self-refreshing environment. The cone as a stack of circles comes as a result of attempting to see in the cone the triangle that is a stack of lines. Each new hypothesis comes out of taking an aspect of an old theory as a projective model for the materials of the new situation. It comes, as it were, in answer to the question, 'Find the familiar x—the split fibres, the closed environment, the stack of lines—in the unfamiliar y.' From the point of view of the situation, the new idea is a potential solution to a problem of explanation or action. From the point of view of the metaphor, the new idea is a further elaboration.

These examples illustrate two ways of proceeding in the displacement of concepts:

—beginning with a problem and searching for a metaphor which will in its elaboration yield a hypothesis for a solution.
—beginning with a metaphor, elaborating it, and developing the hypotheses it yields.

These are characteristic, respectively, of problematic and speculative inquiry.

PROJECTION

This explanation focuses attention on the use of projective models as a means to new hypotheses.

There is nothing new in the idea that projection can give rise to new hypotheses. In his journal of 1508 Leonardo da Vinci recorded the following passage:

> *A way of developing and arousing the mind to various inventions.* I cannot forbear to mention among these precepts a new device for study which, although it may seem but trivial and almost ludicrous, is nevertheless extremely useful in arousing the mind to various inventions. And this is, when you look at a wall spotted with stains, or with a mixture of stones, if you have to devise some scene, you may discover a resemblance to various landscapes, beautified with mountains, rivers, rocks, trees, plains, wide valleys and hills in varied arrangement; or again you may see battles and figures in action; or strange faces and costumes, and an endless variety of objects, which you could reduce to complete and well-drawn forms. And these appear on such walls confusedly, like the sound of bells in whose jangle you may find any name or word you choose to imagine (Taylor, ed., 1960, p. 57).

More recently, Gestalt psychologists like Wertheimer have recognized the role of projection in leading to new ideas. They point out that new ideas may result from new ways of seeing, specifically 'seeing new things in' old configurations.

What I take to be a new point here is that metaphor, the source *par excellence* of new ideas, is a projective process. In this process projective models for new situations give rise to new ideas. Metaphor represents a more restricted form of projection like the projectiveness of a riddle. We are asked not merely, 'What do you see in X?', but 'Find the Y in X'. Metaphor is a process of taking the familiar as projective model for the unfamiliar, leading in its course to a new way of seeing the familiar as well.

This provides us with a way of distinguishing between the displacement of concepts and the rote, Epaminondas-like use of analogy. In the unintelligent use of analogy, an old theory is carried over to a new situation, in whole or part, without any change in perception of the old theory and without taking account

88

of what is new in the new situation. In the displacement of concepts the old theory is restructured in response to the new situation for which it is a projective model. The notion of projection becomes central to a definition of intelligent learning.

Projection is also of great current psychological interest because of its apparent ability to give access to unconscious material. Projective tests like the Rorschach have been ways of getting at unconscious material, by presenting 'neutral' objects onto which subjects project structures which are more revealing of the subject than of the object. It has often been remarked, *ad nauseam* in recent years, that new ideas require unconscious work (how else, it has been asked, do ideas for solutions to problems unexpectedly 'happen'?). But there has been little or no attention to the connection between projection as a way of unearthing unconscious material and projection as a way of getting at new ideas.

We appear to have several routes of access to unconscious material. One is fantasy, the little playlets in which we are chief actors, that come unbidden to mind. Another is free association, the train of symbolically related thoughts that come in response to a stimulus when we let thoughts come, without attempting to direct them. Projection is a form of restricted free association, in which every association is built around the stimulus projected upon, and is in effect a different way of looking at that thing.

To project onto a thing is a special way of associating to it. All of these processes have in common the fact that we cannot make them happen although we can set up conditions propitious for their happening. They all have a kind of indirection about them, like looking to the side of a star in order to see it more clearly.

They are not ways of interrogating the unconscious. They are ways of letting the mind perform certain tasks, so as to question its results for their unconscious meaning. Seeing a butterfly in a Rorschach figure and seeing a stack of disks in a cone are, alike, ways of letting the unconscious reveal itself in what is seen in something. In both cases potentials are set up for probing the unconscious and for developing new ideas, although in each of the two contexts only one of these potentials is realized. Projection answers to unconscious need and is a sign of the need. It can also be in the displacement of concepts a way of finding the familiar, traditional, in the unfamiliar; and through this a route to new ideas. But it is never a route to new ideas except as it is also the expression of an unconscious need. Something of this will be discussed in a later section of this chapter.

The projective character of the displacement of concepts is particularly apparent in certain sequences of thought where one thought grows out of another as though the thought had a life of its own. The form of theme and variations, or what might be more appropriately called theme and developments, is a case in point. Often each succeeding variation appears to have been built on the one preceding. The first variation may present a motif which was not present explicitly in the theme itself. The second variation may take up this new motif in such a way that it relates to the theme primarily through the first variation.

A similar relationship can be seen in certain sketches by Picasso, part of a long series done together (see Leiris, ed., 1954). The theme of artist and model runs through all three, but each variation on the theme seems to grow out of the preceding one.

In the field of technical invention, similar series are to be found. They can be found, in a particularly striking way, in the following series of designs by Paul Matisse, who began with the problem of designing a new kind of fastener. His first model, which he called a shear-tension fastener, consisted of two bars with meshing, angled teeth. A pin was inserted through the bars, which could not then be drawn apart without shearing the pin.

(1)

The second model was made to provide a fastener which would fasten to the surface of plastic parts. It consisted of two opposite rows of file-like teeth, into which two male parts were inserted. A wedge was placed between the two male parts so that they could not be lifted from the surface until the wedge had been removed.

(2)

The third model consisted of two meshing, undercut spiral configurations that could be meshed or drawn apart with a quarter turn or less.

(3)

In effect, they represented a rotating version of the file-tooth design pictured in (2).

Here, as in the preceding series, each entity gives rise to the next. Given the first shear-tension model, the second can be seen as an answer to the question, 'How can a flat shear-tension fastener be made?' And given the second surface-fastener model, the third can be seen as an answer to the question, 'How can a rotating surface fastener be made?' Each can be seen as having been made on the projective model of the preceding.

These processes do not take place, of course, in a vacuum. The notion that a flat model would be desirable grew out of work on needs for fasteners in plastics. (*Then* a flat version of (1) was sought for.) The notion that a rotating flat model would be desirable grew out of observations about relative ease of surface fastening. But once developed each design became a projective model for what was to follow.

A similar relation is to be found in each of the series of geometrical examples given above. In fact, we can find such projectively generated series not only in designs developed by one man but in much of the history of the development of inventions, forms, and theories, by many men at different times. The subject opened up here is enormous. It will be taken up again, in connection with the evolution of theories, in Chapters V and VI.

My chief point for the moment is that the displacement of concepts gives rise to new hypotheses not only by permitting elaboration of a single metaphor, but in series of hypotheses, designs, and the like, each of which functions as a projective model for the succeeding one.

These comments about the emergence of new hypotheses from metaphor have been descriptive. They have had to do with the way such processes work rather than how they ought to work. But there is also considerable interest in a normative theory of discovery. One kind of interest shows up in industry and government, for which 'creativity' and 'innovation' have become, for a variety of motives, catchwords of the first importance. Another kind of interest goes back far into the history of logic. Descartes was pointing out in the seventeenth century that syllogistic logic, the logic of Aristotle, could never lead to anything new since it was confined to spelling out the propositions contained in familiar premises. He set out to provide a logic, more explicitly, a set of directions for the conduct of the mind, which would provide a valid route to discovery as well. Since then, there has been a running, though much interrupted, controversy over the possibility of a logic of discovery. John Stuart Mill denied its possibility, for example, on the grounds that 'a man cannot bethink himself of that which suits his purpose' and logic presumably can apply only to what is under the possibility of direct control.

Some years ago Karl Popper published his *Logic of Discovery* and, more recently still, N. R. Hanson published *Patterns of Discovery*. But these titles are, in a sense, misleading. Popper turns out to be concerned with stating the conditions under which a discovery can be validated after the fact; and Hanson, with the conditions under which the proposal of a hypothesis can be shown to be plausible after it has been generated. Almost always, in their consideration of processes of discovery, philosophers have found it necessary to take an after-the-fact view and to concern themselves with the conditions under which something or other, once generated, can be justified.

Toulmin, in *The Philosophy of Science*, devotes a chapter to discovery. He begins by asking,

> If we are to know what questions to ask about physical theories, we must be clear to begin with what kinds of things count as discoveries in the physical sciences. What is it for something to be 'discovered' in physics? . . . what does such a discovery amount to? (Toulmin, 1960, p. 17).

But we quickly find him saying,

> The question can be put in another way; if, in physics, someone claims to have discovered something, what sort of demonstration will justify us in agreeing that, whereas this was not previously known, it can now be regarded as known? (ibid., p. 17).

And we are back with problems of justification.

In this case the transition from prospective theory of discovery to retrospective theory of justification has gone unnoticed. When the transition is made explicitly the usual defence for the need to concentrate on justification has been that genetic processes, processes leading up to the formulation of hypotheses, are the exclusive subject-matter of psychology. It has never been clear to me why the study of such processes must be exclusively psychological. In fact, it is a kind of study that psychologists (with the rare exception of a writer like Wertheimer) do not engage in, perhaps because psychologists tend to find the normative consideration of discovery too unscientific.

If there is room for anything called a logic of discovery, it would have to have the following properties:

93

It would consist of statements of some generality, reflecting regularities in its subject-matter.

These general statements would be independent of persons and of individual cases.

They would be normative, 'ought' statements.

And they would relate, by their content, to the plausibility of the hypotheses to which they refer. (There is no problem about saying how hypotheses ought to be generated, if *any* hypothesis will do.)

In current scientific practice does anything corresponding to these criteria exist? There is certainly no set of rules for the formulation of hypotheses. The very notion would make a research man shudder. But there is an understanding of good scientific practice relating to the formulation of new hypotheses which might be called a 'wisdom' literature. It tends to be handed down vertically from professor to student, or horizontally from colleague to colleague. Often the individual investigator discovers it for himself. It is implicit and informal and loose, in comparison to logics of justification. Nevertheless, it meets most of the criteria outlined above. Attempts to make it explicit can be found in writers as different as Osler, Cannon, Beveridge, and Polya.

In a similar vein, comments about the role of metaphor in the formulation of new hypotheses could contribute to a sort of wisdom literature. They provide some basis for general, normative statements relating to the generation of plausible hypotheses. For example,

1. Processes of metaphor are functional in the generation of new hypotheses. Attention should be paid to them, even when they appear irrelevant.
2. Old theories which turn out to be inapplicable to a new instance may still be useful in the generation of plausible hypotheses if they are taken as projective models for the new situation.
3. You can listen to intimations or disregard them. When they

relate to the appropriateness of a metaphor they are often useful as clues to its fruitfulness as a source of plausible hypotheses.

4. Hypotheses are apt to grow out of one another, if they are allowed to do so, each taken as a projective model for the next.
5. It is useful to ask theoretical, even philosophical, questions, like 'What happens when paint flows in a brush?' even when the question does not lead to a rigorous answer. Such questions can lead to the generation of metaphors from which plausible hypotheses can be developed.
6. The crossing of disciplines is useful as a means of generating metaphors fruitful of good new hypotheses.
7. It is worthwhile paying attention to the literal language in which theories are formulated. This is often suggestive of metaphors underlying the theory and therefore of further elaborations or of related metaphors, yielding new hypotheses.

Statements like these need to be filled in with examples, as I have tried to do in earlier sections, in order to lose their empty ring.

At a lower level of generality, within specific disciplines and problem areas, there is great value in pointing to various familiar theories as projective models for new situations—as in noting how helpful it is to think of a new electrical circuit in hydraulic terms. This is a matter of good common practice in scientific inquiry and in inquiry generally.

But there are qualifications to be made.

The matter seems to me to be analogous to playing a musical instrument, at any rate more like this than like a manual for the assembly of a new rifle. It is possible to write about good practice in playing the piano or even about good practice in interpreting the Beethoven sonatas. Such a book could be useful to those listening to piano sonatas. It could direct their attention to aspects of the playing which become meaningful to them, although they might miss them otherwise. It could be useful in making understandable, and therefore more tolerable, the sort of thing the pianist does in playing and learning to play.

It would have a certain utility, but a very limited utility, for the pianist himself. For example, it would not teach him how to play the piano. It would not take the place of practice, or of a good ear, or of the drive to become a concert pianist, or of sensitivity to the emotional language of the music. Without these other things, it would be quite useless. Moreover, the things it would tell the pianist to do he would not necessarily be able to do merely by willing to do them. In this sense, such a book might be extremely frustrating. But it might confirm him in certain directions he had already tentatively begun. It might make him more attentive to certain things in himself which he would otherwise brush aside as irrelevant. It might make more understandable and therefore more acceptable to him the sort of process he found himself going through.

EMOTIONAL BASES OF PROCESSES OF DISCOVERY

Most of these qualifications to the use of a logic or heuristic of discovery have to do with emotional undercurrents that are essential to the drama of the emergence of new ideas. These aspects of the process escape direct control.

How do we come to perceive novelty, for example? From one point of view the new, in the form of the strange, the puzzling, the confusing, simply forces itself in, like a baby's angry cry. But often the new turns out to have been available for observation long before it was actually observed. Investigators had been exposed to phenomena associated with the vulcanizing of rubber, the effect of penicillin moulds on bacterial cultures, the presence of gummy polymers in the bottoms of test tubes following certain chemical reactions, long before these phenomena were seriously observed and 'discovered'. Why did most investigators fail to notice them? Suddenly, the familiar Gestalt figures (illustrated on p. 7) can be seen in ways that are dramatically different. Once seen, the new view is perfectly obvious and had obviously been there all along.

What needs to be explained is inattention to the new. But there is no mystery here. Selective inattention maintains the prevailing Gestalt. It would be a vague, disturbing world if our rabbits were constantly turning to ducks and our vases to profiles. It would be a wonderful world, a schizophrenic world, in which nothing is the way it seems. By screening out disruptive novelty, selective inattention makes for conviction, as well as for simplicity, obviousness, and sanity. 'Closed minded' and 'narrow minded' describe not only pathological conviction but conviction generally. And conviction is necessary for directed action.

This virtually equates an extraordinary capacity for attention to the new with an extraordinary incapacity for action. And, in fact, the world has been full of inventors, writers, and speculators, including great ones like Leonardo, who have been victims of their capacity for attending to novelty. Such men appear to be incapable of sustained directed action. They embrace one project with enthusiasm only to be taken up by another equally engrossing, that shuts out all memory of the first. At their worst, they are unable to finish anything.

But some innovators combine, paradoxically, the capacity for selective inattention essential to action and the openness to disturbing novelty essential to discovery. They manage at once to be open and closed. They take a directed course while at the same time, in another corner of their mind, they attend to irrelevances, to the unexpected, to what does not fit. Innovation demands concentration on a single theme of action while other themes are held in suspense.

In our culture 'novelty', 'the new', 'innovation', 'creativity', have taken on highly positive emotive meanings. But we are easier in our mind talking about the new than actually experiencing it. It is always a painful and wrenching experience to confront a confusing situation and to break with a way of structuring it that had been deeply held, however joyous and exhilarating the resulting insight may be. It is no surprise, then, that a law of least

97

change operates in all the interactions among our structures, the world, and us. Conservatism is our characteristic pattern. The little skirmishes with the new on which we focus attention are rare exceptions in our lives.

The extremes of creativity and novelty lead to madness—not only inability to distinguish fantasy from reality but inability to form structures that could be the basis for a perception of reality at all. The novel is the unexpected. Our very concepts, of objects, people, emotions, values, depend on regular expected sequences of perception, action, and perception. Our concepts can be understood as series of expectations of what would be perceived, given some perception, if a certain action were taken. If our world were suffused with novelty, none of these expectations would be fulfilled. There would be no reality. There would be no directed thought.

Openness to novelty, then, is openness to experience that is dangerous and potentially destructive. It involves what Dr Raymond Hainer calls 'coming apart'. Our integration as a person is threatened when we are forced to break a deeply held structuring of experience. The deeper it is, the more intimately tied to other theories, the more threatening it is to break it.

So that attentiveness to novelty, in the sense in which I have been discussing it, involves a form of personal risk-taking that is very high. The inventor, the innovator in theory, is most willing and able to put his own way of looking at the world (and therefore his concept of himself) on the block. I am not sure whether this implies an extraordinary underlying security in the sense of self—a kind of ground-bass, as Valéry describes it, repeating 'I—I—I' in the face of the barrage of otherness set up by novelty in the world; or a looseness as to self, an involuntary slipping in and out of personal integration, that has more to do with loss of a sense of self than with security.

In this coming apart, this slipping in and out of ways of looking at things, there is something like childlikeness. The projection in metaphor, the riddle-like, 'Find the x in y' quality of it is playful. When we call children 'imaginative', we refer to their prodigious ability to see everything in everything, horses in chairs and dolls in clothes-pins. This playful projection is at the heart of the displacement of concepts. There is also something playful in the innovator's perpetual 'What if . . .?' and 'Wouldn't it be nice if . . . ?' These questions signify being intrigued with fantasy and a willingness to stay long in a world of fantasy. There is something childlike, too, in the fascination with the unexpected behaviour of things that is characteristic of invention. The inventor is apt to dally with things long before he can justify his interest in them.

This playful quality of the process of discovery has received considerable study and deserves more. But it would be wrong to think of playfulness, even tinged with regression, as the characteristic mode of discovery. Characteristically, with its oscillations between wrenching pain and unexpected joy, the process is full of strong emotion.

It is always a social process. It consists of a series of events that take place with reference to other people, present or internalized. In this sense, it is a drama. Like most dramas it has to do with love and hate and it has its central themes or plots. Here the themes are 'showing them' and 'gaining their love', and often the two are mixed.

I once had an invention fantasy which, although trivial in itself, illustrates the 'show them' theme. I was driving home after a meeting with a technical man (I will call him Foster) whose practical competence I find most impressive. In the fantasy Foster and I were in the same room. I was demonstrating a new device, a kind of roller that applied contact paper to the wall by means of a heat-sensitive adhesive. Foster looked on, awestruck, saying, 'It will revolutionize the wallpaper industry.' Suddenly, with a real pain in the stomach, I realized there had to be a source of heat in the roller. My mind flipped through a number of possibilities (an electric cord that could be tripped over, thermoelectricity) and then struck on a two-compartment system I had once seen in a foot warmer in an army surplus store. When the membrane between the two compartments was broken, lye and water combined to give off heat. Again I was applying the roller to the wall, the roller heated this time by the two-compartment system, and again Foster was saying, 'It will revolutionize the wallpaper industry.'

This fantasy has as its basic theme showing, and showing up, someone whose approval I badly needed. Invention was a means of 'showing him' I could do it. The invention extracted admiration from him and was to some extent at his expense. It had a large component of hostility.

There was also in the fantasy a kind of hedonic continuum, a moment to moment stream of pleasure and pain that determined the fantasy's direction. 'Showing' Foster was pleasant. The intrusion of reality (lack of a source of heat) was painful. 'Solving' the heat problem and regaining the illusion of Foster's admiration was pleasant again. I felt goaded in the direction of this pleasure. There was also a kind of balance between self-sustaining fantasy and the intrusion of reality. The fantasy's self-sustaining power, rooted in temporary pleasure and security, gave the basis of the invention. The intrusion of reality and the subsequent flowing of the fantasy around it (like a stream flowing around an obstacle), gave the remainder of the invention. If the reality had been so strong as to interrupt the fantasy altogether, or if there had been no consideration of reality at all, there would have been no invention.

I have encountered many situations in which a process of invention seems to have followed a dramatic pattern similar to the pattern of this fantasy.

A new man entered our product group and suffered a new member's usual insecurity. We were at work on a chemical approach to a certain cleaning problem. The new man was a mechanical designer. He was so irritated by our chemical approach that he set about doing the same thing mechanically, on his own. His mechanical approach succeeded and replaced our chemical one, to our mixed chagrin and admiration.

A research director who had devised a new kind of pump wished to get a highly inventive engineer to work on it. The engineer took it up and worked on it for several months. During that time he worked at convincing the research director the concept was unfeasible and should be abandoned. When the director finally agreed, the engineer insisted on working a little longer. Finally he returned to the research director with a changed design of his own which he said would make the concept feasible. He had 'shown' the research director and shown him up, and established the new product as *his*.

In still another case, a junior man and a senior man worked together on a project for a year's time. The collaboration was in the end highly productive. But the better part of the junior man's effort was aimed at showing that the senior man was mistaken in his basic approach. The collaboration ended with a dispute over authorship of the device, the junior man believing that he had finally been responsible for the successful result, triumphing over the obstacles the older man had put in his way.

In contrast to the dramas of productive hostility, there are dramas of productive love. General Doriot, Director of Research and Development for the Quartermaster Corps during World War II, once said that the way he got a technical project accomplished was to 'find a good man who liked me and tell him I was up against it'. Some of the great men of industrial research, like Whitney in the early days of the General Electric Laboratory, inspired love and respect in their technical men, who worked and invented to gain love and respect for themselves.

These dramas of innovation are two sides of the same coin. They present invention either as showing up someone who is feared, and forcing approval and admiration, or as gaining the love of someone else who is loved. Sometimes the dramas are mixed: the 'other' may be both hated and loved, and the invention may be aimed both at showing him up and at gaining his love.

I cannot resist the temptation to relate this to the behaviour of children with their parents or parent-figures, and to relate the two dramas of invention to styles of loving and hostile behaviour to loved and hated parents. The drama of invention is a continued acting out of family dramas. But the elaboration of this view lies beyond the scope of the present work, which has aimed only at sketching in some of the emotional themes underlying the displacement of concepts and the generation of new ideas.

I have touched on the disruptiveness of novelty and the risk in taking it seriously; playful and aggressive aspects of innovation; and the role in innovation of dramas of love and hate. My examples have been drawn from technical innovation, because this is where the bulk of my recent experience lies. My guess is that these themes are to be found in the generation of ideas in other areas as well.

SCOPE OF THE DISPLACEMENT OF CONCEPTS

Most of this chapter has been spent discussing ways in which the displacement of concepts leads to the formation of new hypotheses. Nevertheless, discovery is only one of its contexts. In this section we will look at some of the other contexts in which the displacement of concepts appears, its relation to similar processes in perceptual and behavioural learning, and, in general, its scope.

I have already presented evidence to suggest that its scope is enormous, comprising, in effect, all new concept formation. But it is strange, in view of this, how little attention the process has actually received. Apart from Cassirer and his followers very few writers have related it to concept formation. How has it managed to escape notice? There is our tendency, discussed in earlier chapters, to take an after-the-fact view of knowledge; we tend either to ignore the birth of our knowledge or to read its results back onto its beginning. But there are other relevant causes of neglect.

For one thing, there is the curious working of the process over time. In one sense, the displacement of concepts is indifferent to time. In an hour the metaphor of the house as a theatre, for example, can be made, explored, and corrected, with great richness. The process of displacement reflected by 'cold war' has beef going on over about the last fifteen years. The displacement on concepts implicit in 'light travelling' has taken centuries—at least from pre-Platonic times to contemporary discoveries that light can be regarded as the 'movement' of states of information—and it is still continuing. The metaphor of concepts as things, like trees and fish, seems to have been with us, with relatively little development, since the beginning of Western culture.

When such processes move so slowly relative to our own processes of thought and action, it is no wonder that we tend to be unaware of them. The time period of the displacement of a theory is often so great as to make it part of the background against which our thinking happens rather than an object of attention within our thinking. (Again, it is hard to resist the analogy to processes of geological and biological evolution.)

Why does the displacement of concepts vary so in time-scale?

In order to explain this, I am compelled to adopt an apparently circular argument. As I have been saying, we are often blind to the displacement of concepts; we are unaware of our metaphors. We talk about being level-headed, having our feet on the ground, feeling bitter, and so on, without realizing that our language is something less (or more) than literal. What we are inattentive to, we cannot deliberately change. The covertness of metaphor protects it from change.

It is hard to realize the effectiveness of this sort of protection because, once we become aware of a metaphor, we continue the process of displacement so easily. Let it be pointed out that our psychologies are partly based on atomic theories, and we are able to continue the displacement, modify it, or even abandon it. When we realize that our theories of education result in part from the displacement of theories of nutrition—as indicated by phrases like 'digesting a course', 'intellectual growth', and the like—we are able to question them. It is hard to believe that mere concealment from view can have been such an effective obstacle to change. But covert metaphors are like sheltered islands, where earlier forms of life persist because they are protected from the rigours of natural selection.

The displacement of concepts tends to go unnoticed because of its long time span, and it tends to have so long a time span because it goes unnoticed.

Does a metaphor's going underground affect it other than by making it more resistant to change? Freud maintained that thoughts and wishes tend, on becoming unconscious, to gain greater intensity and generality and to seek various forms of symbolic expression. In a similar way, certain metaphors of our culture, as they go underground, intensify and become more generalized. In the United States the notions of 'selling' and of the 'machine' have been displaced to almost every field of human life. Persuasion is conceived on the projective model of sales ('selling yourself', 'being sold on an idea') and there is hardly a process which is not conceived on the model of the machine ('the machinery of politics', 'mechanisms of thought'). These metaphors have wormed their way into as much of the culture as they can, and they can do this so well just because they are hidden. It is very much the same with theories of Christianity which have been displaced since medieval times to our notions of the world, government and man. These phenomena would appear as a kind of pathology of the displacement of concepts, if it were not for their great utility.

Sometimes the displacement of concepts is masked, rather than merely covert. It appears under the guise of the simple application of a concept to its instances or, again, as an after-the-fact use of metaphor to explain or elaborate a concept already developed. The vast majority of the metaphors of ordinary speech have lost their overt metaphorical character. When we say, 'This is a bitter feeling', it sounds like 'This is a rectangle'—that is, like the simple application of a concept to one of its instances. Because of this similarity in the apparent grammar of statements, and the faded metaphors of ordinary language, the displacement of concepts masquerades as application of concepts. This may happen even when the displacement is made for the first time. An engineer may say 'This liquid is a kind of spring' without being aware that he is saying anything different in kind from 'This liquid is a kind of acid'.

Again, there is a commonplace after-the-fact use of metaphor. A teacher presents a theory of the brain as a kind of central telephone exchange. He has other ways of thinking about the theory. If he developed the theory for himself, the metaphor may not have played any part in this development. It serves merely as a model to make clearer, more easily graspable, a theory which might otherwise be obscure. On the other hand, we sometimes use metaphors as devices for explaining theory when they were actually essential to the formation of theory. In discussing a theory of genes, the lecturer may say, 'Think of it, if you will, as a kind of code,' when in fact he has no other way of thinking of it. Something like this happens when scientists teach theories of sub-microscopic phenomena in terms of mechanical models or when biologists teach theories of natural selection in terms of models of human competition.

Behind both of these ways of masking the displacement of concepts is the familiar tendency to see thinking in terms of its products rather than its processes, the tendency to look at formed concepts which are being applied or explained rather than at partly formed concepts in process of formation.

Putting these motives for not looking at the displacement of concepts aside, we can turn to other related areas. One such area is the process of generalization, by which I mean the process of moving from the grasping of an individual to the formation of a concept which can apply to that individual and to others as well. I am familiar with Boston, but I have the concept of 'a Boston' just as people speak of 'another New York', or 'another Hitler'.

Generalization includes abstraction, as when we 'take out' of a concrete experience the concept of the properties of a rhombus. The concept of 'rhombus' need not exist prior to its being taken out of the experience, just as there need be no antecedently held general concept making up our notions of 'Boston' and 'Hitler'. At first there is only a grasping of individuals. In these cases, generalization involves displacement. If we call San Francisco the New York of the West, San Francisco does not suffer in the metaphor from having no George Washington bridge. New York functions here as a projective model, and its usefulness in the generalization can be grasped before it can be spelled out or defended.

All of this is in a sense obvious. If the extension of concepts to new kinds of instances involves displacement, the extension of our grasping of individuals must involve it too. Our previous discussion of the displacement and extension of concepts is a discussion of generalization. Generalization from the grasping of individuals is simply a special case of it. The non-obvious point is that the grasping of individuals is not clearly a concept at all, so that its displacement is not clearly a displacement of concepts.

This difficulty is of particular interest as it relates to child learning. Children form concepts from antecedents which, because of their lack of form and generality, it would sometimes be hard to call concepts at all. A theory of individuals and a theory of abstraction are involved here as well as a theory of concept formation in children. Such theories would be related, in a family resemblance way, to the present theories of displacement.

Another process related to the displacement of concepts is the process of perceiving one thing as another. Here again we could speak simply of the displacement of concepts if there were any concepts, properly speaking, to be displaced.

The Gestalt psychologists, along with Wittgenstein and his followers, have concentrated primarily on *seeing* one thing as another. The familiar Gestalt figures and the Rorschach figures present ambiguous visual forms. This 'seeing' may or may not involve the emergence of novelty. In the examples given earlier, the ducks and rabbits in the figures relate to familiar concepts. On the other hand, when someone first saw the sun as a kind of wheel, something new emerged. 'Seeing . . . as . . .' may simply be a way of describing the displacement of concepts from the point of view of the concept-structured situation rather than from the point of view of the concept displaced. But it is a matter of assumption both that all concept-structured situations involved in concept formation are perceptual and all perception of one thing as another involves concepts, as I have been using the term.

To make matters more complex, it may be that all seeing can be understood as 'seeing as'. Hanson suggests as much in his *Patterns of Discovery*:

> I do not mean to identify seeing with *seeing as*. Seeing an X-ray tube is not seeing a glass-and-metal object as an X-ray tube. However, seeing an antelope and seeing an object as an antelope have much in common. Something of the concept of seeing can be discerned from tracing of 'seeing . . . as . . .' . . . Consider again the footprint in the sand. . . . One can even imagine cases where 'He sees it as a footprint' would be a way of referring to another's apprehension of what actually is a footprint (Hanson, 1958, p. 19).

Whether or not we agree with Hanson, all identification of perceptual situations involves finding a familiar projective model in the situation. Where novelty emerges, the projective model is itself seen differently so as to function projectively for the situation. But as we were concerned just now with the borderline of concepts and individuals, so we are concerned here with the borderline of concepts and perception. A theory of perception would be required to clarify the relation of 'seeing—as—' to the displacement of concepts.

Similar comments could be made about certain kinds of behavioural learning. There is a kind of learning in which patterns of behaviour shift from one situation to another. A child who has learned to swim in a pool learns for the first time to swim in the ocean. He has material to work with, patterns of expectation and response. But as he first encounters waves and the buoyancy of salt water, everything he has learned to do must shift. He must learn and adapt, but he does not start from scratch. His old way of swimming is displaced to the new situation.

Learning theorists have had difficulty in accounting for this kind of old-new behaviour. Their approaches have been in many ways analogous to the approaches of theorists of concept formation.

Some have attempted to break down behaviour into smaller bits and to reduce novel behaviour to recombination of old bits. Others, especially in stimulus-response theory, have concentrated on learning as the 'stamping in' of response, without concerning themselves much with the origin of the behaviour stamped in. Some have related it to physiology, and others, to chance. Still others have treated behavioural learning in terms of hypothesis formation and verification, making explicit their links to theories of concept formation. Here, too, there are tendencies either to the denial of novelty or to its mystification.

Learning through shift of behaviour, with emergence of new behaviour built on the projective model of the old, is particularly striking, again, in children. As he learns to ride a big bicycle after he has learned to ride a little one; as he learns for the first time to run, or to eat with a fork; in virtually all learning, the child can be seen shifting old patterns to new situations, using the old as projective model for the new, just as he treats his first encounter with school through the metaphor of his family.

Here, too, we can ask whether we are dealing with a special case of the displacement of concepts or with a behavioural analogy to it. If we believe there can be no learning without concept formation, we will lean towards the former view.

These three areas related to the displacement of concepts—the formation of concepts from the grasping of individuals, perceiving one thing as another, shifting behaviour from one situation to another—can be seen either as special cases of or as analogues to the displacement of concepts, depending on the room made for concepts in our theories of individuals, perception, and behaviour.

PART TWO

The Conservative Function

CHAPTER V

The Conservative Function of the Displacement of Concepts

INTRODUCTION

Up to this point we have been asking how new concepts are formed and new theories built. We have looked at the displacement of concepts for its role in the formation of new theories and the generation of new ideas. We have been concerned, in short, with its *radical* function.

But the process can also be seen as a *conservative* one. It is a way of carrying over what is old in our theories. It permits us to deal with the new while at the same time retaining as much as possible of our past structuring of the world. Both points of view can be brought together in the statement that the displacement of concepts is the means by which we bring our past to bear on our future so as to permit us to profit by our experience without being saddled with it.

The conservative function is to be seen most clearly in the development of theories. Old theories underlie new ones. When old theories are displaced to new situations, *all* aspects of the old theories tend to locate themselves projectively in the new situations. Epaminondas-like, aspects of the old theory may be taken as projective models for the new situation without being changed themselves in the process. They become fixed as assumptions

about the new situation, often unrecognized, carried over uncritically from the old theory. Aspects of the new situation may be
overlooked or misconstrued in a way that damages action or
explanation based on the displacement.

We have already discussed at some length the displacement of
the concept of the 'cold war' to the current international situation.
In the following passage, drawn from a *New Yorker* article,
Richard Rovere points to one of the assumptions which has been
carried over uncritically along with it:

> The term 'Cold War' was given currency by Walter Lippmann,
> the greatest of the period's historians, and if it has been apt in
> some respects, it has been unfortunate in one major respect:
> *it has led people to imagine themselves in a specific conflict that must
> end in defeat for one side and victory for the other.* But Mr Lipp-
> mann, along with most of the makers of American strategy, has
> always realized that this is not the case. When, in the late
> forties, our best diplomatic and military planners began to take
> the full measure of Communist power in the world, they were
> chiefly concerned with how the United States and the free
> nations of Western Europe could survive and remain free.

In my terms, the carrying over of this assumption is a direct
result of the displacement of the theory. It is an aspect of the old
theory transferred, without change, to the new. It is part of the
conservation of the past characteristic of the displacement of
concepts.

This chapter will illustrate conservatism in the displacement of
concepts. We will examine a number of theories which belong
to common sense—theories of decision-making, theories of the
mind, theories of understanding, and theories of love. In each
case, we will relate the commonsense point of view to its counter-
part in philosophical or psychological theory, and then trace it to
earlier theories from which it had been displaced.

Our approach will be a kind of metaphorical analysis. The actual
language of a theory contains metaphors which are vestiges and
signs of the old theories whose displacement helped to form the

new one. These metaphors are clues to the identity of the old theories. If we hear talk of 'weighing alternatives', 'balancing one against the other', and so on, we can guess that the speaker is working from the projective model of a balance scale. In order to discover whether the new theory is actually a displacement from this old one, we look for assumptions transposed from the old theory uncritically to the new situation. If these assumptions are found in the new theory, particularly if their presence is undefended and unexplained, then a presumption is established that the old theory does underlie the new one. In the case of the balance scale, for example, we would expect to find the assumption that deciding involves a comparison of *two* sides which are set off one against another. This assumption is to be found, undefended, in much of our talk about deciding as well as in theories of deciding adduced by philosophers and psychologists.

Quite apart from questions of genesis, this approach is useful analytically in focusing attention on critical assumptions which might otherwise be overlooked.

Nevertheless, it raises a number of difficulties. Metaphors are sometimes merely ornamental. They may serve to explain to the reader something the author has come to understand in a completely different way. Or they may be merely conventional, the residue of a once-live metaphor which has ceased to be functional in the theory. Moreover, even if we have established through metaphor that a new theory came to be formed through displacement of an old one, it is by no means easy to state precisely what that old theory is. For example, the theory reflected by the metaphor of the balance scale can be expressed at more than one level of generality: 'weighing objects on a balance scale', 'comparative weighing' or 'comparison'. Two quite different notions, like 'weighing on a scale', and 'debate', may overlap in the assumptions to which they lead. Or the new theory and the old may both share common assumptions which arise from still another source.

I know of no way of resolving these problems, except by showing that in explaining and predicting assumptions found in the new theory, the theory suggested by the metaphor is effective, and more effective than another. The metaphor of the scale can be shown to be neither conventional nor ornamental if it points the way in a new theory to a number of hidden and undefended assumptions. And it can be shown that the notion of the scale, rather than of a debate, is functioning as a projective model for the new theory if the two 'sides' in question are treated as passive and unchanging rather than autonomous and active.

THEORIES OF DECIDING: THE SCALE; THE USE OF TOOLS; GROUP PROCESSES

'Deciding', as I use it, includes making up your mind, deliberation, making practical judgements, and in general the whole range of processes of thought associated with deliberate action. These processes are by no means uncommon, so that we have in general currency more than one theory of how decisions or practical judgements are made. In response to the question, 'How do you make up your mind?', few of us would be at a total loss.

In this connection, philosophers, of course, have seldom been at a loss and there is a current of theories about deciding that runs from Plato and Aristotle, through the Church fathers and the medieval theologians, to such modern writers as Descartes, Bishop Butler, Locke, Hume, Bentham, Kant, and on to contemporary philosophers and psychologists like Stevenson, Lewin, Köhler, Sullivan, and many others.

In the following pages we shall dip into these writers from time to time, not to provide anything like a rigorous history of theories of deciding, but to locate certain counterparts in formal theory to the informal theories of our common sense. It will be easier in these formal theories to trace the metaphors and assumptions we use and make in ordinary discourse.

THE SCALE

How are decisions made? A common kind of answer, perhaps the one that comes most readily to mind, is the following:

> You have to decide whether to do one thing or another—whether to get married or not, for example. So you compare the two possible actions. You think of all the likely consequences you can, if you do one or the other. You try to estimate all the advantages and disadvantages of each course of action. And you choose the one whose advantages outweigh its disadvantages.

Where does this answer come from? It seems obvious and straightforward, if uninspired; but its obviousness fades immediately if we ask what is meant by 'comparison' of actions, or by advantages 'outweighing' disadvantages. It is not difficult to find in this description the projective model of weighing on a balance scale.

In this example, 'outweigh' provides one clue, but there are many other phrases in our language for deciding that also reflect a displaced theory of weighing: 'deliberation' (itself, originally, 'weighing'), 'weighing arguments', 'giving due weight to a consideration', 'balancing arguments against each other', 'a weighty piece of evidence', 'tip the scales in favour of . . .'

While in our time the symbol of the balance scale continues to work powerfully, it has become so conventional that it is difficult to take seriously. Its most common form in Western culture has been the 'scales of justice'. Werner Jaeger, in his *Paideia* (1945), pointed to the similarity between Old Testament justice, with its 'eye for an eye', and the Greek concept of justice. This he associates first with Solon's concept of human law and then with the concept of divine justice or Fate in Greek tragedy—a balancing of joy and suffering in the human condition. He sees the 'hubris' of Greek tragedy as tipping of the scales, due to excess of human pride, which must be balanced by an equal amount of human suffering. The stain that marks royal families and nations in Greek tragedy signifies such an imbalance. The material of the tragedies, the inevitable working out of the curse, is in effect a balancing of the scales. The metaphor of the scale, written large, becomes the basis of divine and human justice and, with the Greek fusing of natural and moral law, the basis of world order as well.

It could be argued that the metaphor of the scale lives on in Plato's notion of justice as a balancing of elements in the human soul and in Aristotle's concept of the 'mean', the 'balanced life' —as well as in such modern counterparts as 'balanced diet', 'balanced education', and 'well-balanced man'.

What is of greatest interest to us, however, is the post-seventeenth-century concept of the balance scale as a mechanical process, a particular form of the Newtonian machine. In this form, evidence of the scale can be found in many formal and common-sensical theories of deciding.

A whole series of passages reminiscent of it runs through Jeremy Bentham's *Principles of Morals and Legislation*. For example:

> An action then may be said to be conformable to the principle of utility ... when the tendency it has to augment the happiness of the community is greater than any it has to diminish it (Burtt, ed., 1939, p. 792).

Or again,

> Still more difficulty would a man find in assuring himself that with regard to those [motives] which are ranked under the name of neutral or indifferent, the effects they have had have *exactly balanced each other, the value of the good being neither greater nor less than that of the bad* (ibid., p. 826).

In the same spirit, there are many comments about the 'greater' and 'lesser' 'weights' of arguments and the 'opposing forces of motives'.

> It can scarcely ever happen, therefore, that an act really mischievous shall not have some part at least, if not the whole, of the *force of this motive to oppose it* ... (ibid., p. 837).

Similar passages can be found in Hume's *Enquiry Concerning the Principles of Morals*:

> In many cases this [the giving of moral praise and blame] is an affair liable to great controversy: doubts may arise; *opposite interests may occur; and a preference must be given to one side, from very nice views, and a small overbalance of utility* (Melden, ed., 1955, p. 281).

In these passages deciding is a weighing of elements—motives, acts, principles—in which the heavier (the one with 'greater force') gets translated into action or receives approval. Deciding is a process not of balancing the two sides but of determining which is the greater or more forceful. It is presented, at least in Bentham, as a special case of an opposition of Newtonian forces:

> ... a man ... is frequently acted upon at the same time by the force of divers motives; one motive ... acting in one direction; another motive ... acting ... in the opposite direction (Burtt, ed., 1939, p. 831).

By far the most convincing illustration of the role of this metaphor for Bentham, however, is his view of the manner in which questions of action *ought* to be resolved.

> An action then may be said to be conformable to the principle of utility ... when the tendency it has to augment the happiness of the community is greater than any it has to diminish it (ibid., p. 792).

To determine this tendency,

> Take an account of the number of persons whose interests appear to be concerned, and repeat the above process with respect to each [i.e., sum the values of the pleasurable and painful consequences in question]. Sum up the numbers expressive of the degrees of good tendency which the act has, with respect to each individual ... do this again with respect to each individual in regard to whom the tendency of it is bad upon the

117

whole. *Take the balance; which if on the side of pleasure, will give the general good tendency of the act* . . . (ibid., p. 804).

The principle of utility requires that actions be weighed on a hedonic balance scale.

This simple picture is complicated by other metaphors underlying passages like the one above. One is the metaphor of accounting, summing up, and comparing columns of figures representing debits and credits. Another is the metaphor of the judicial process. Bentham's chief work is called 'Principles of Morals *and* Legislation'. He seems to regard the formal judicial process and the process of individual deciding as special cases of the same general process, at least as far as normative issues are concerned.

> . . . justice, in the only sense in which it has a meaning, is an imaginary personage, feigned for the convenience of discourse, whose dictates are the dictates of utility applied to certain particular cases (ibid., p. 830).

Given the scale's traditional role in theories of justice, it is understandable that the metaphor figures so prominently in Bentham's theory of deciding. Theories of accounting are also partly based on the scale as phrases like 'balance the books' suggest.

In Bentham, then, there is a coming together of several metaphors which present a similar pattern and should therefore give rise to common, or at least overlapping, assumptions. The metaphor of the scale works here both directly and indirectly through the displacement of other theories whose development it had once affected.

Bentham's *Principles* represents a formal version of the informal view of deciding with which this section began. Bentham is one of the philosophical ancestors of our own obvious common sense, and reflects more clearly our own involvement with the metaphor of the scale. But the fact that the scale has passed into common sense in our own time does not mean that it is no longer present in formal theories of deciding as well. One of the most celebrated of contemporary moral theorists is Charles Stevenson.

His *Ethics and Language* presents the fashionable view that moral judgements are expressions of attitudes, capable of being supported by facts, but themselves neither true nor false. As Stevenson presents the patterns of reasoning by which moral disagreements are resolved, the metaphor of the scale appears again:

> The argument might then continue about whether the alleged attendant evils were evils, or about whether these were *outweighed by the good consequences* (Stevenson, 1944, p. 127).

> An ethical judgement is often supported by the systematic presentation of a whole body of beliefs, in which specific (factual) conclusions are subsumed under more general ones, and *each conclusion is weighed with regard to its probability* (ibid., p. 129).

> But another possibility remains, which many writers earnestly strive to realize: that of *giving the arguments which may support 'the other side' their full attention, and balancing them off against those which support the aims that are advocated* (ibid., p. 129).

As a follower of the moral tradition of Hume and Bentham, Stevenson inherits, apparently unknowingly, the dominant metaphors of eighteenth-century theories of deciding.

Given this presumptive evidence for the role of the scale in theories of deciding, what assumptions would we expect to find associated with it? Because the scale has been treated since the seventeenth century as a special form of the Newtonian machine, it shares with other mechanical systems some of the assumptions to which its displacement gives rise. These will be discussed later on. But there are a number of assumptions peculiar to the theory of the scale itself.

Objects Come to the Weighing Process ready to be Weighed

Objects are brought to the scales. They do not have to be invented in order to be weighed. In a sense, they are given for the weighing process; from the point of view of the weighing, they are assumed. The issue is not how they came to be, but how much they weigh in comparison to one another.

In theories of deciding based on a displaced theory of weighing, we would expect actions—alternatives, principles, motive and the like—to be treated as given for evaluation. Problems of invention or formulation would be ignored.

But this is true of such commonsensical theories of deciding as we discussed earlier. When we say, 'Deciding is a matter of determining which of two alternatives is the more advantageous', we take the alternatives as given. We focus on evaluation rather than on discovery, on the process of deciding whether to do this or that rather than on the process of thinking what to do.

Similarly, Hume, Bentham, and Stevenson are concerned exclusively with actions already completed or with alternatives of action already formulated. Bentham begins, 'When a man has it in contemplation to do a certain action . . .' Utilitarianism as he presents it is a way of deciding whether or not to do something, *after* you have thought of what you might do. Hume is also concerned only with evaluation of actions, motives, or dispositions, which he assumes as given for the purpose of his analysis. Stevenson's patterns of analysis are always cases in which an act, an alternative, a principle, or whatever, is given with the example. In all cases, there is no reference to the process by which possible actions get formulated in the first place. They are somehow given for the analysis, just as things are given to be weighed. There is no recognition that discovery enters into deciding, and no defence of the omission.

Any theory of deciding is open to criticism for such an omission. In the case of Bentham, who presents utilitarianism as a code for regulating one's conduct, the omission is particularly unfortunate. Once a problem has been formulated in terms of doing our duty versus securing our own happiness, to take a classical kind of example, the 'answer' usually seems obvious. The function of the code is to rationalize a conclusion already arrived at. But the peculiar difficulty of certain practical situations which makes them 'moral', or at any rate serious, has to do with the situation's resistance to formulation in terms of clear-cut alternatives of action. Through its omission of problems of formulation, utilitarianism turns out to be applicable only when it is unnecessary.

This omission cannot be traced to the displaced theory of weighing alone. Stuart Hampshire has called attention to moral philosophy's exclusive preoccupation with retrospective evaluation. If we look at actions only in an after-the-fact way, we also treat them as given for evaluation. But the influence of this preoccupation is not incompatible with the role of the scale. Both tendencies are present in the theories we have reviewed, and they are mutually supportive.

In the Course of the Weighing, Objects do not Change

As far as the scale is concerned, an object goes out as it came in. If change occurs, the weighing does not cause it.

We would expect a theory of deciding based on a displaced theory of weighing to treat objects of decision as unchanging.

When a process of deciding answers the question, 'Should I do this or that?' and answers it by listing and evaluating advantages and disadvantages of two courses of action, its conclusion is a decision to do this or that, or neither; not a change in the formulation of the alternatives.

Similarly for Bentham, deciding consists in determining what the consequences of an act are likely to be, evaluating those consequences in terms of their pleasurable or painful tendencies, and choosing the act whose pleasurable tendencies are greater. The 'acts' ('beating an innocent man', 'challenging a man to fight', 'bestowing a large sum on a private charity', to take some of Bentham's examples) remain the same throughout. For Stevenson, 'rational' evaluation of an act, where it is possible, consists in adjusting beliefs which support attitudes of approval or disapproval towards the act; when one attitude comes to outweigh the other, we are justified in approving or disapproving the act. Attitudes towards the act are 'redirected', but the act is not represented as having changed.

This assumption of unchanging objects of decision runs counter to many observations about deciding. It is at odds with every situation in which we say, 'I have come to look at it differently'. What begins by looking like 'beating an innocent man' may come to be seen as 'avenging a wrong'. Like patches of colour in a painting, projected actions, when they are juxtaposed, influence one another. 'Behaving courageously' may come to look like 'compromise' when the right comparisons are made. Much of our best practical thinking takes the form of questioning the formulation of the problem, so that *all* alternatives are changed.

> How should I deal with the boss? Should I fight him head on, or should I try to get around him? There are risks in both cases, and more or less likelihood of getting what I want ... but should I be treating him as an antagonist at all? What are his interests in the matter? How am I affecting him?

Such processes are precluded by the assumption of unchanging objects of decision. And the effects of this assumption are not merely theoretical, for our theory of deciding influences our actual deciding.

Similarly, one weighing does not affect the next. Each weighing is independent and self-contained; results are the same regardless of what precedes or follows. In Bentham and Stevenson, and in the commonsense view we have been discussing, each instance of coming to a decision is taken on its own merits. There is no recognition of chains of decisions as attempts to cope with a common theme. There is no sense of decisions representing a *development*. But many of our decisions cluster around common themes, and much of our deciding is what it is because of the deciding that preceded it. The notion of intellectual or moral growth requires as much.

On a Balance Scale, Things are Weighed in Twos

Because of the very structure of a balance scale, weighing is always a comparison of two things or sets of things. If more than two things are to be dealt with, they must be dealt with in terms of sets of twos.

Similarly, for Hume, Bentham, Stevenson, and for the commonsensical theories we have been discussing, deciding is always seen primarily as a matter of choosing between *two* alternatives, actions, sides, arguments or inclinations.

We observe this tendency in drama, from Hamlet's 'To be or not to be' to Jacobowski's 'There are always two possibilities'. We find it in Kierkegaard's 'Either/Or' and in hundreds of other similar titles in our literature. It is enshrined in the 'exclusive or' of our logic. It is tied to our Western mania for comparison and competition.

There has been opposition. Philosophers have proposed multi-valued logics as alternatives to classical two-valued ones. They have commented on a host of dualisms—mind/matter, emotive/referential, subject/object. Most often, these dualisms have been accepted as a framework for discussion of philosophical problems. Less often, the dualisms have been questioned.

So far as I know, there has been little questioning of our tendency to see deciding in twos, in spite of its significant consequences. It forces us to see deciding as 'supporting one side against another'. It brings the form of the legal process, the debate, the argument, into the very heart of our moral life. The view of deliberation as internal dialogue, in which one side is pitted against another—in the Christian framework, a 'good' side against a 'bad'—forces us to see internal conflict, not to speak of conflict among several individuals, as a 'zero sum game' in which one side wins at the expense of the other. It does not leave room for deciding as a form of synthesis in which eventual decision reflects the interests which had been seen as conflicting. It reinforces the Romantic notion that major decisions involve sacrifice of a part of the self, and therefore it has a tendency to intensify the difficulty of decision.

At the very least, it leaves out of account in theory and in practice the part of deciding that has to do with the elaboration of new 'third' possibilities. This helps to explain in another way why in theories of deciding processes of discovery and invention have been so much ignored. Two people mainly concerned with holding up their sides of an argument are unlikely to develop a new point of view, although they are sometimes forced to do so. To innovate is to change, and change can be seen from this standpoint as defeat. Similarly, in personal deliberation a man is unlikely to come up with something new if he is primarily concerned with choosing one of two views he already has in mind. Furthermore, because it is difficult to force anything like the full breadth of practical situations into the mould of two opposite sides, emphasis on duality makes for oversimplification.

It would be absurd to claim that this emphasis on duality, with all its consequences, results exclusively from the covert influence of the metaphor of the balance scale. The balance scale itself seems to have been a mechanization of the process a man goes through when he compares objects with his two hands. We still say 'on the one hand' and 'on the other'. We are, after all, bi-symmetrical. The balance scale was built on the projective model of two-handed comparison just as dualistic theories of deciding were built on the projective model of the balance scale—a model which has left its traces in uncriticized assumptions of the givenness of alternatives, the priority of evaluation over discovery, unchanging 'acts', and deciding in twos.

THE USE OF TOOLS

How are decisions made? Another sort of answer, also compatible with our ordinary ways of speaking and thinking, runs as follows:

> We find reasons and use them to *support various points of view. By bringing them to bear* on possible actions we *work out* a conclusion. These various *devices* enable us to *make up our mind.*

These phrases, drawn from the manipulation of things and specifically from the use of tools, suggest another source of displacement to our theories of deciding. Similar metaphors characterize our language about problem-solving and thinking generally. We speak of 'intellectual skills', 'the materials of a problem', 'mental instruments or devices', 'chiselling out a theory', 'driving home a point', 'puncturing an argument', 'a mind like a razor', 'dull and sharp people', 'intellectual skill', 'shaping an argument', 'building a theory', 'carving out an area', 'splitting hairs', and the like.

In formal theories of deciding, such phrases turn up even more frequently. In philosophers as diverse as Butler, Kant, Hume and Bentham, there is talk of 'using' reason as an 'instrument', in achieving ends. In more recent times, John Dewey has described a way of thinking in which the meaning and value of terms is determined through analysis of their use as 'instruments' in solving problems. Dewey's instrumentalism has had wide influence, as evidenced by this passage from Stevenson.

. . . instruments whereby one person supports a view that he is recommending to another, or criticizes a view that the other is recommending to him (Stevenson, 1944, p. 130).

Here the decider is seen as a sort of craftsman of the mind. Problems, ideas, attitudes, and beliefs are his materials and reason is his tool. With more or less skill he plies the deciding trade.

Where deciding is seen in this way, a number of assumptions are to be found. Two of these are as follows:

A Tool is Used to do Something that has been Anticipated

We get a putty knife because we know ahead of time that we want to fix a window, a hammer because we want to drive a nail. If we see deciding in terms of the use of tools, it too becomes a manipulation of instruments to achieve an anticipated goal. All problems become a species of technical problem. In some cases, as with Charles Peirce in *The Justification of Belief* (1960), processes of practical reason which arise because of the absence of an appropriate goal, or because of a conflict of goals, get to be seen as the adjustment of means to achieve a supergoal: the removal of the conflict, or the attainment of agreement, or the alleviation of doubt. In this way we need never ask what to do but only how to do it.

This way of looking at deciding leaves out the emergence of the unexpected and the influence of the process on the agent. It makes deciding closed- rather than open-minded. There is, however, a way of using tools so that the material's reaction to the tool suggests the next steps. This provides a metaphorical basis for a more open-ended sort of Instrumentalism, of which there is some evidence in Peirce and Dewey.

A Tool Changes other Things, but is not Changed in the Process or, to the Extent that it is, it is Considered Defective

A tool, then, is a privileged thing. Where the metaphor of the tool underlies theories of deciding, writers tend to regard 'reason', 'intelligence', beliefs, or the agent himself, as privileged. Thus, when we speak of 'changing our attitude' or 'sharpening our ideas' or, with Stevenson, 'shaping attitudes through beliefs', there is something that remains unchanged and for all practical purposes beyond the possibility of change. This is reassuring. Because of the unobtrusive safety of the part of ourselves we view as doing the changing, we can tolerate the idea of change.

Stevenson finds it essential, for example, to keep scientific method inviolable, while pointing out the emotive and frequently non-rational character of deciding. By treating scientific method or its common-sense equivalent as an instrument to be used in shaping attitudes, he is able to shield it from the possibility of change. The same can be said of Freud's fierce adherence to his concept of scientific method, and later to his own analytic method, both of which he treats as tools for probing our unconscious lives. What a man would preserve from change, he makes into a tool.

This privileged character extends to the tool-user, as well. As we usually see it, a man cutting a piece of wood with a saw is changing the wood and is not being changed himself. He wants to control the material, not to be controlled by it. He has a kind of psychological distance or detachment from the material. Quite literally, the tool is a way of giving him this distance. Similarly, seen in terms of a displaced theory of the use of tools, deciding becomes a process in which the agent manipulates aspects of himself—attitudes, beliefs, or what have you—preserving in the process his distance and his sense of control. While he 'shapes his attitudes', 'adjusts his beliefs', and 'probes his motives', he regards these things as other than himself. We cannot casually 'adjust our beliefs' if we are deeply involved with them. To talk of 'our' changing 'them' would be inappropriate. The change would be better described as a change in us.

The same distance and detachment in the relationship between the 'craftsman' and his 'material' appear in theories of leadership based on the metaphor of the tool. When people are regarded as instruments to get things done, then theory of leadership and actual leadership manifest a tool-like distance between superior and subordinate.

But it is doubtful whether the actual use of tools always lives up, or down, to this view of it. The most sensitive and accomplished craftsmen tend to eliminate this distance between themselves and their material. They are apt to regard the wood or the metal as a living thing with needs and feelings of its own and to let the material direct them as much as they direct it. In our culture, however, this is a deviant view. The dominant view, so dominant as to seem partly constitutive of Western thought, treats tool-using—and by displacement, deciding—in terms of the adjustment of means to a foreseen end; the privileged, unchanging character of the instrument; and distance between the agent and his material.

Because the metaphors of the scale and the use of tools come out of deliberate individual activity with things, I call them 'deliberate' metaphors. There are others like them, also present in our theories of deciding. One of these comes from the displacement of theories of the diagnosis and cure of disease, and finds its expression in phrases like 'finding the symptoms of a problem', 'cleaning up a situation', 'finding the cure of an evil', and by the gradual movement of words like 'therapy', 'prognosis', 'treatment', and 'disease' into situations not ordinarily treated as medical. This displacement carries with it the assumption that 'cure' consists in a return to 'normalcy'—that is, to the *status quo*. Still another deliberate metaphor results from the displacement of theories of the making of works of art.

In the language of deliberate metaphors, there are some common features. We speak of 'making' a decision, 'trying' to decide, 'undertaking' a judgement, and the like. These words are part of the language of doing: we *make* a pie, *try* to climb a mountain, *undertake* a job. 'Making' a pie and 'making' a decision are not 'making' in the same sense. In these deliberate metaphors, we displace theories of doing to deciding, carrying over in the process a set of assumptions that includes the following:

1. Deliberate action is an active process; actions are things done rather than things that happen. Similarly, when we think in terms of this metaphor, we see deciding as something done rather than something that happens to us.
2. Actions are goal-directed. They are undertaken for the sake of some end—the curing of a disease, a finished work of art, or the like. When deciding is understood through a displaced theory of deliberate action, the decision or the judgement is taken as the end or aim of the process. Because of this goal-directed character, the process takes place in a kind of Aristotelian time, with a discrete beginning, a middle, and an end. Symbolically, Aristotle made the process of 'making' so central to his own view of deliberate action that in his theories action and deliberation are inseparable.
3. In deliberate action an agent undertakes a goal-directed process and works it out from beginning to end. There are passive things he works on—his materials, the disease he cures, the thing he fixes, the clay he moulds. When deciding is seen in this way, an agent is set off against the materials he manipulates—the rules, concepts, alternatives, of action,

and the like. The active decider contrasts with the passive elements of self he manipulates.

This way of thinking is central to our notions of 'deciding' and 'decision'. What is a decision unless it is something 'made', something 'worked out'?

But these assumptions are by no means self-evident. Deliberation need not be seen as an exclusively active process. A current in our literature, from Plato to Poincaré, has always emphasized the 'happening' in practical thinking—the surprises, unexpected changes, and inspiration. Perhaps novelty and change come about only through happenings in which a person feels himself at least momentarily passive. This is certainly part of most descriptions of what it feels like to get an idea or to utilize a change of character. Nevertheless, when we see deciding in terms of a displaced theory of deliberate action, we attempt to eliminate unexpected novelty and unprepared change. We leave no room for happenings.

SOCIAL PROCESSES

How are decisions made? Still another familiar theory runs as follows:

> When we are undecided, we are subject to pressures from a number of conflicting inclinations and beliefs. Each insists on having its say. Finally reason tells us which, if any, is the one to follow.

In this passage, which describes a personal decision, it is not difficult to recognize the underlying model of a social process. The passage itself has a rather overtly metaphorical ring, but in our language of deciding there are many less obvious metaphors drawn from social processes. Consider:

I told myself . . .
I took myself in hand . . .
I asked myself . . .

My conscience won't let me . . .
Impulse got the upper hand . . .

In addition, many of the key terms used to refer to deciding, terms like 'conflict', 'resolution', 'deliberation', and 'decision', are regularly applied both to individual and to social processes. These metaphors, if metaphors they are, have become so conventional that it is surprising even to ask whether an individual's decision and a group's decision are decisions in the same sense.

When deciding is seen in this way, it embodies a kind of social animism. The mind is divided into autonomous elements or 'persons'. These elements have purposes of their own and may either conflict or agree. They retain their identity throughout the process of deciding.

We are apt to treat animism as a primitive, or at least an old-fashioned, mode of thought. It is no longer fashionable to hold with the animistic faculty psychology of the nineteenth century, in which the mind was thought to be made up of personalized entities such as Will, Reason, Inclination, and the like. But it is clear from phrases like those quoted above that social animism has invaded common sense about deciding. It has invaded it in many new forms, however. We think of deciding in terms of debate, war, games, drama, and business.

What is more, writers of formal theory have come with increasing frequency to treat the mind as a kind of society. They personalize aspects of the mind, but emphasize the 'social' rather than the 'animistic' part. The notion of the mind as society can be found in the writings of George Herbert Mead (1934), who treated the self as a coming together of internalized 'others'. It can be found in Freud in the famous myth of id, ego, and super-ego and in less famous aspects of his thought—for example, in his comment that he had come to think of every sexual relation as involving four 'persons'. It is equally visible in the writings of socially oriented psychiatrists like Horney and Sullivan. In fact, it is difficult in our culture to find any thinking about the mind untouched by the notion of mind as a number of different selves which succeed one another in consciousness, vie with one another, hold internal dialogues, and come to decisions. It is difficult to think about the mind without the displacement of social theory.

For this very reason the question could be raised whether metaphor is involved at all. Just as Bentham coupled the judicial process with individual deciding, and other philosophers now treat deciding as a species of scientific judgement—without any sense of metaphor—so many contemporary writers would deny that displacement is involved when they treat individual deciding in terms of social process. Most philosophers and psychologists would agree in calling mythical or metaphorical the older forms of social animism—faculty psychology or the Christian view of deciding as a war of good and evil elements, for example—but they would deny the metaphor in our use of words like 'conflict' and 'decision' for both individual and group processes.

Stevenson again presents an interesting, not to say inviting, example, and one which will help to clarify the role of the social metaphor in our own theories of deciding.

In the section in which he deals for the first time with personal deciding, he repeats all that he has previously said about interpersonal deliberation.

> The question is complicated in its details. People make their ethical decisions in many different ways. In outline, however, it can be answered quite simply, and in a way that follows so naturally from our previous considerations that it brings with it little novelty (Stevenson, 1944, p. 130).

Why does he think so?

> When does a person feel the need of making up his mind about what is right or wrong? Not, certainly, when his attitudes speak with one voice, urging him in a definite direction. . . . Rather, the need of a personal ethical decision arises from a conflict of attitudes. The individual's attitudes do not speak with one voice, but urge him both this way and that, with the

net result of leaving him in a painful and inactive state of irresolution (ibid., pp. 130–131).

Note the 'attitudes . . . speaking with one voice'. Stevenson quotes Dewey to support his view that individual moral deliberation involves conflict, and then concludes,

> From this it can be seen that the personal aspects of ethics are not very different from the interpersonal ones. The former involve conflict; the latter, when they are controversial, involve disagreement in attitude. Conflict and disagreement in attitude are much the same, since conflict occurs (to speak roughly but not ineptly) when an individual disagrees in attitude with himself. So the personal aspects of ethics reveal the same opposition within an individual that has previously been seen within a group (ibid., p. 131).

There is some oscillation here. Phrases like 'to speak roughly but not ineptly' and 'not very different' suggest that Stevenson is aware of the analogical relationship between personal and social deliberation and is engaged in exploring the metaphor. Phrases like 'reveal the same opposition within an individual which has previously been seen within a group' give the lie to this and suggest that he thinks the two are literally the same. This view gains support from his inattention to the metaphors in 'speak with one voice' and 'disagreement in attitude'.

But there are significant differences between personal and social deliberation, particularly where 'conflict' and 'resolution of conflict' are involved. Their relative obviousness suggests that Stevenson is, in fact, treating personal deliberation on the metaphor of social deliberation. Otherwise, how can we explain his *neglect* of the obvious relevant differences? The difficulty is not that he is governed by a metaphor, but that he is governed by it covertly and uncritically.

People may conflict with one another in at least two different ways:

    (i) they may hold incompatible aims, or
    (ii) they may behave towards one another in a hostile way.

The relation between these two kinds of conflict varies. People may be hostile to one another because they hold incompatible aims, but they may also generate incompatible aims in order to display their hostility. They may even display hostility towards one another when they can point to no incompatible aim other than 'winning the fight'.

Fighting is available as one way of dealing with social conflicts. Discussion, modifying aims, or showing that they are not incompatible, is another. In the first sense one party to a conflict can 'win' in the sense of preventing the other from realizing his aims. In the second sense, the conflict may be more or less overt in that the hostility may be more or less revealed.

These statements, which seem well enough founded when applied to social deliberation, generate an interesting series of assumptions when they are applied to personal deliberation.

1. Conflicting aims are attributed to different parts of the self

This is what is implied by phrases like 'speak with different voices' and even 'make up your mind'. Dewey, in the passage Stevenson quotes, speaks of conflict as 'a situation in which an individual wants incompatible things'. But what about the step by which these incompatible wants are attributed to 'different voices', or to 'different parts' which must be then made up, or to different 'selves' which 'disagree' and then must be brought to 'agree'? Stevenson makes this assumption fairly explicit in his comment that individual conflict involves 'disagreement with oneself'. But it is by no means clear what this means, much less that it is true.

2. Parts of the self may display hostility towards one another

3. One part of the self can defeat another by making the other renounce its aim or by preventing the other from realizing its aim

4. Disagreement between parts of the self can be settled by the modification of aims or by reasoning about aims so as to show that they are not, after all, incompatible, or they may be settled by force

133

The last three assumptions have a rather special status. Stevenson does not make them explicit. Yet he would have to make them explicit if he were to treat personal deliberation as an instance of social deliberation or as substantially identical to it. It is far from clear what might be meant by 'one part of the self displaying hostility towards another part of the self' or 'one part of the self winning out at the expense of another' or 'the settlement of a personal conflict by force'. There may be something about personal deliberation which is something like what is expressed in these assumptions, but they are certainly not literally applicable to it. At the very least, evidence is required where none is provided.

All of this is particularly important for Stevenson because of his central claim that some kinds of ethical conflict or disagreement are not susceptible to settlement by the use of beliefs and are settled, if at all, only by persuasion or the use of force. What does 'persuasion' or 'the use of force' mean as applied to personal deliberation? Significantly, when Stevenson comes to give an example of personal conflict and resolution of conflict, although he uses the language of interpersonal deliberation ('fortifying one side or the other', causing 'one set of attitudes to predominate over the other'), he chooses a case where conflict is settled by means of beliefs. He does not face the issue of what 'non-rational settlement' would mean for personal deliberation.

Although it may be useful to treat personal deciding on the projective model of social deciding, this uncritical use of it serves an illegitimate purpose: it permits Stevenson to act as though it were obvious that his theory applies to personal as well as social deliberation when in fact the burden of proof is on him to show that it does.

There are other questionable assumptions to which we are led, along with Stevenson, when we treat personal deliberation under the metaphor of social deliberation. Consider the notion of a 'decision' itself. In a group a decision—an executive's 'yes' for example—is, in fact, an overt action. It is relatively discrete as an action; it results from previous discussion; and it is often the partial cause of something that follows. We are accustomed to see an individual's private decision as the result of previous deliberation and the partial cause of an action to follow. We treat the decision as a kind of 'act'—'an act of the mind', it is often called. But are these things so obviously true of an individual's private decision? Are we aware of anything discrete which could be called an 'act of decision'? Do such acts, if they occur, result from previous deliberation? Are they the partial cause of actions that are undertaken thereafter?

Why do we assume, for example, that an individual's private 'decision' is a cause of change rather than a recognition of change? We say 'I have decided' and 'I will decide', but are we ever aware of a decision as such, when this is a private and not a social event? Perhaps personal decisions are always gratuitous in that they are mere reflections of changes that have already taken place.

Something similar can be said about the moralists' notion of 'crucial decision'. Crucial decisions are thought to be full of significant consequences for the decider and for his character; they are taken as the special subject-matter of at least one kind of moral philosophy. But again, does it make sense to talk about crucial decisions when they are taken as private rather than social events? When a man says in a group, 'I will join the Communist Party', he is making a crucial decision whose consequences for him are great. If he makes the remark in the United States in a room full of peers who believe what he says, and who are not themselves communists, he will begin to be treated as a communist, or at least an incipient one, and there will be significant change in his life. Similarly, if a man becomes a thief, and serves a jail term, he gets to be regarded as a thief, his life changes, and he changes in response to the reaction of others to him. But is there a sense in which a private decision can directly exercise an influence on the character of the decider? The point about a 'decision' made overtly in a group is that it is already an overt action. It can begin having consequences on the way other people view a man, and on his own behaviour in response to them. What, if anything, corresponds to this effect when the decision is a private one not yet reflected in overt action?

Again, I do not mean to deny the possibility of private decisions or even of crucial private decisions. My point is that with little reflection the obviousness of the assumptions associated with these terms disappears. Both the assumptions and their apparent obviousness result from a displaced theory of social deciding.

So far, however, nothing has been said about the variety of theories of social deciding which have been displaced in this way. Changing theories of group behaviour, from the additive atomic notions of the eighteenth century to the field-dominated notions of some social theorists of our time, are of interest in this connection. So are theories of social activity like war, debate, and drama. Of these one of the most important is theory of government.

Common usage frequently includes the metaphor of the mind as a state and deciding as government. We use phrases like:

self-control
control of impulse or inclination
He governed himself well, or badly.
He dominated his feelings.
He kept himself in check.
He allowed himself considerable freedom.
He was ruled by reason.
He is easy, or hard, with himself.
He gave in to himself; or, he mastered himself.

It is not unusual to hear descriptions of deciding which run along the following lines:

I was aware of a number of possible alternatives and of a number of interests that demanded attention. Some were more insistent than others. I gave each due consideration, evaluated the consequences of following them, and finally decided in favour of my more enlightened long-range interests. By an effort of will, I forced myself to carry out this decision.

The underlying model is that of a royal court, in which the anonymous 'I' is king and the conflicting 'interests' are subjects crying out for preference.

Government-based theories of deciding have a long and hon-
ourable history in our culture. Plato, with his myth of the soul
as state, became the first and most eminent representative of the
tradition. As usual he is far more explicit than most about the
metaphors underlying his theory:

> I propose therefore that we inquire into the nature of justice
> and injustice first as they appear in the state and secondly in the
> individual, proceeding from the greater to the lesser and com-
> paring them (Baker, ed., 1927, p. 63).

When Plato moved from the myth of the state to the human
soul, he formulated the famous three-part division of 'sensual',
'spirited', and 'intelligent' elements, each with its own autonomy
and its own claims to dominance. He treated justice for an individual—that is, the good life—as the proper organization of the
three. The soul is a government; a man is just only if the elements
of the soul are in their proper places.

In *The Allegory of Love*, C. S. Lewis traces the development of
social, and specifically government-based, theories of mind from
the Greek to the medieval world. His primary concern is with
the emergence of allegory, the narrative of personified states of
mind, as a method. But he regards allegory as a literary reflection
of a tendency in men, at the dawning of Christian culture, to
think of their own minds under the metaphor of interacting
persons.

> The really good man, in Aristotle's view, is not tempted. . . .
> The ease and pleasure with which good acts are done, the
> absence of moral 'effort' is for him the symptom of virtue.
>
> Now when we turn to the moralists who lived under the
> Roman Empire, all this is changed . . . they were certainly more
> conscious of a difficulty in being good. 'Fight the good fight'—
> how oddly the words would sound in the *Ethics*! Under the
> Empire, they are on every moralist's lips.
>
> . . . Whatever the causal order may be, it is plain that to fight
> against 'Temptation' is also to explore the inner world; and it

is scarcely less plain that to do so is to be already on the verge of allegory. We cannot speak, perhaps we can hardly think, of an 'inner conflict' without a metaphor; and every metaphor is an allegory in little. And as the conflict becomes more and more important, it is inevitable that these metaphors should expand and coalesce, and finally turn into the full-fledged allegorical poem (Lewis, 1958, pp. 59–61).

Lewis believes that for similar reasons the allegorical method attracted the poets of courtly love: they were helpless to describe so internal a passion without social metaphor.

It is as if the insensible could not yet knock at the doors of the poetic consciousness without transforming itself into the likeness of the sensible: as if men could not easily grasp the reality of moods and emotions without turning them into shadowy persons. Allegory, besides being many other things, is the subjectivism of an objective age. When Lancelot hesitates before mounting the cart, Chrétien [de Troyes] represents his indecision as a debate between Reason which forbids, and Love which urges him on. A later poet would have told us directly— though not, after all, without metaphor—what Lancelot was feeling: an earlier poet would not have attempted such a scene at all (ibid., p. 30).

It is not so far a cry from Chrétien de Troyes to such philosophers of the modern era as Bishop Butler, Hume, and Kant. Chrétien had spoken of reason 'forbidding' the knight what love had 'urged' him to do. In Hume we find talk of a similar relation between reason and impulse:

Reason, being cool and disengaged, is no motive to action, and directs only the impulse received from appetite or inclination, by showing the means of attaining happiness or avoiding misery (Melden, ed., 1955, p. 285).

And Kant speaks of,

. . . the purpose of nature in its appointment of reason as the ruler of our will (ibid., p. 296).

while warning that,

> Reason is not, however, competent to guide the will safely with regard to its objects and the satisfaction of all our needs . . . (ibid., p. 297).

In Bishop Butler, the place of reason is taken by conscience:

> It is from considering the relations which the several appetites and passions in the inward frame have to each other, and, above all, the supremacy of reflection or conscience, that we get the idea of the system or constitution of human nature (ibid., p. 208).

In these passages the mind figures as an hierarchical society and deciding as government. On this basis, we would expect to find in these writers and others like them a set of shared assumptions:

(i) There are a number of elements in the mind which vie with one another for control.

(ii) These elements differ in rank and prestige just as the elements of a government do.

(iii) There is one element—reason, conscience, or something else—which is in the nature of a naturally constituted elite.

(iv) Rationality consists in the rule of this superior element.

These assumptions appear in theories of rational deliberation expressed in Plato, Christian theology, and the *Roman de la Rose*, as well as in philosophers like Butler and Kant. They underlie the commonsense equivalent of these theories. They are inherent in our notions of the rational, the saintly, and the gentlemanly life.

The theory of government expressed in these assumptions is that of the fitting rule of a naturally constituted elite. Plato holds such a theory both for the state and, displaced, for the individual. As a theory of government, this belief in the right rule of a natural aristocracy has frequently come under fire, and has as often re-emerged. In modern times it has taken its most severe drubbing

139

at the hands of the British social contract theorists and egalitarians —men like Locke, Hume, and James Mill—who have pointed out the doubtfulness and the inherent evil of the assumption of a natural elite. But we can find in Locke and Mill, and in their followers in theory of government today, a steadfast conviction in government by natural elite, as that theory is displaced to the mind. For the British view of virtue and rationality, from Bishop Butler on, is nothing more than a natural aristocracy of the mind. We can guess that the transposed theory, protected by its covertness, provided a hidden outlet for that British love of natural aristocracy with which overt social ideals conflicted. Can it be found as well in the fierce rationalism of a Shaw or a Russell?

In the last two centuries these assumptions have come to be questioned in theories of deciding as well. Whence comes the special rank of reason and conscience? What is meant by their 'rule'? Why should they rule? Hume contributed to undermining this view—although he continued to express it—in his questioning of the meaningfulness of a conflict of reason and will, and in his famous dictum that 'reason is the slave of the passions'. Contemporary philosophy and psychology have come to question the special positions of reason and conscience. The Positivists, current followers of Hume, have pictured moral conflicts as nonrational oppositions of feelings and attitudes in which reason is a mere instrument. Their view of the mind is more nearly egalitarian. Much current psychology seems to have had the effect of undermining reason's special position, presenting it instead as after-the-fact rationalization of impulse.

The natural aristocracy of the mind has had its drubbing, but only at a lag. It has survived its parent theory.

THEORIES OF THE MIND: MECHANISM AND DYNAMISM; ATOMISM

In some ways we have already begun to speak of theories of the mind, for theories of deciding and theories of the mind go together. The scale implies a mechanical view of the mind, and the social theory of deciding implies a social theory of mind as well.

In this section, however, we will examine two more bodies of theory: atomism and the correlated theories of mechanism and dynamism. Atomism and mechanism are related, in that some forms of atomism make it a species of mechanism. The three theories together suggest that psychological theories have evolved by displacement from physical ones.

MECHANISM AND DYNAMISM

These two ways of looking at the physical world have had long and honoured histories in formal and commonsensical physics and, through displacement, in theories of the mind. In the following passage, Harry Stack Sullivan opposes them:

> I use the word dynamism, you will observe, where other psychiatrists often use the term mechanism. Mechanism has never suited me because it always suggests a Diesel engine. And the one thing we are sure of in interpersonal relations is that there are processes which are dynamic; they are not static mechanical entities. These processes have something in them of the element of energy and they are very apt to go on until something in the way of a goal, a terminal state, is reached, whereupon they cease for the time being and show no trace until they are next called forth (Sullivan, 1956, p. 5).

Sullivan contrasts mind as machine with mind as dynamic process. In so doing, he is fighting a traditional battle in a new arena. The debate has taken many forms. In metaphysics, as far back as Descartes, it took the form of a conflict between mechanism and such adversaries as idealism and vitalism: the world as machine versus the world as vital process. In physics itself, the conflict involved Newtonian mechanics and the field physics of the nineteenth century.

In the late nineteenth and twentieth centuries, the conflict invaded theories of mind, society, the person, and perception—

in short, theories of everything human. On one side it included, among others, associationists, Pavlovians and behaviourists; and on the other, Gestalt theorists, dynamic social theorists, and depth psychologists.

In many ways, therefore, the metaphor of the machine has had more discussion than any other. It has had so much criticism that in some quarters it is no longer fashionable. Nevertheless, it continues to operate covertly in theories of mind, so much so that Sullivan's comment is almost rare as a piece of insight into metaphors underlying theories of human behaviour.

MECHANISM

The notion of mechanism in its metaphorical role is far from a simple thing. Theories of the physical world have had a dominant role in displacement to theories of mind. As theories of the physical world have changed, so have the theories of mind to which they had been displaced—but at a lag. The notion of mechanism, according to which the physical world is treated as a machine, has had a point of origin and a history.

Ideas of natural processes served as metaphors for theories of mind before the development of the view of the world as machine, and some varieties of mechanism operated as metaphors underlying theories of mind before the emergence of modern theories of the machine. In Bishop Butler, for example, we find the idea that our nature is adapted to virtue as a watch is adapted to measure time. Similar views were expressed, explicitly and covertly, by the deists. But here the machine is infused with purpose, with final causes, and so is Butler's machine-theory of human nature. What I call mechanism, however, is specifically the Newtonian world machine. It has been described as follows:

> In mechanics the future path of a moving body can be predicted and its past disclosed if its present condition and the forces acting on it are known. Thus, for example, the future paths of all planets can be foreseen. The active forces are

Newton's gravitational forces depending on distance alone. The great results of classical mechanics suggest that the mechanical view can be consistently applied to all branches of physics, that all phenomena can be explained by the action of forces representing either attraction or repulsion depending only upon distance and acting between unchangeable particles (Einstein and Infeld, 1938).

Consider now the following passage in Bentham:

When a man has it in contemplation to engage in any action, he is frequently acted upon at the same time by the force of divers motives: one motive, or set of motives, acting in one direction; another motive, or set of motives, acting as it were in the opposite direction. The motives on one side disposing him to engage in the action: those on the other, disposing him not to engage in it. Now, any motive, the influence of which tends to dispose him to engage in the action in question, may be termed an impelling motive: any motive, the influence of which tends to dispose him not to engage in it, a restraining motive (E. A. Burtt, ed., 1939, pp. 831–832).

The language of the passage clearly suggests a mass being acted upon by opposing forces—a balance scale, or a car on a track, subject to pushes in opposite directions, one of which would make it 'engage' with another car. The world referred to sounds like the Newtonian world of masses, forces and distances, except that it is the world of the mind.

The general and standing bias of every man's nature is, therefore, towards that side to which the force of the social motives would determine him to adhere. This being the case, the force of the social motives tends continually to put an end to that of the dissocial ones; as, in natural bodies, the force of friction tends to put an end to that which is generated by impulse (ibid., p. 842).

Here there is juxtaposition of the covert and the explicit use of the mechanical metaphor. The explicit use is clearly intended as

143

a pedagogical device, an 'explanation.' But the mechanical meta-phor is already functioning covertly (in 'bias', 'motive', 'force') as a basis for the theory it is being used explicitly to 'explain'.

Bentham's language is not strange to us. We, too, speak commonly of:

> Mental forces.
> Impulse.
> An act of mind.
> Restraint.
> Motives.
> Inclinations.
> Mechanisms of thought, perception, feeling.
> Adherence to a principle.
> Inertia.

We, too, are capable of whole passages of thought about the mind which, with a few replacements, could be applied verbatim to a machine:

> His feelings drove him to produce many ideas which served as motives to action. They were coupled with impulses which broke all restraints and propelled him into activity. . . .

It is clear in these passages, I think, that Newtonian mechanics is being displaced rather than directly applied to the mind. Literally, force implies acceleration. Do we mean that an idea has acceleration when we say it has force? Neither we nor Bentham would refuse to call love a motive because it produces no visible motion. People have tried indeed to apply Newtonian mechanics directly to mind, and to everything else. Materialists and mechan-ists, from Helmholtz to the Vienna Circle, have defended the programme of reducing all theories to some form of mechanical theory. Freud's famous 'project' of 1895 was such an attempt. But we do not have to adhere to the mechanists' programme in order to speak of mental forces and impulses, and generally to conceive of the mind as an enclosed space in which masses move and affect one another in the manner of the Newtonian machine. Deprived of this way of talking we would find ourselves quite at a loss, even though we might laugh at the explicit view of thoughts as masses in the Newtonian sense.

If these verbal clues show that our theory of the mind is based in part on a displaced theory of the Newtonian machine, there are a number of assumptions we should find ourselves (and Bentham) making.

Determinism

It is a prime characteristic of the Newtonian machine that its operation is in principle entirely predictable. Each state of the machine is causally related to the one that follows. From a full knowledge of its state at any one moment, its state at the next moment can be inferred.

When we talk of mental mechanisms and forces, there is a corresponding suggestion that events of the mind are inherently predictable. Given enough information about motives, impulses, inclinations, and the like, we are able to say what people will do. Our informal theories of mind are so vague, it is unclear whether we assume all mental events to be predictable. In Bentham, however, this point is quite explicit.

> Nature has placed mankind under the governance of two sovereign masters, pain and pleasure. It is for them alone to point out what we ought to do, as well as to determine what we shall do. On the one hand, the standard of right and wrong, on the other the chain of causes and effects, are fastened to their throne. They govern us in all we do, in all we say, in all we think: every effort we can make to throw off our subjection, will serve but to demonstrate and confirm it (Burtt, ed., 1939, p. 791).

In this paragraph there is evidence of the metaphor of the mind as government as well as the metaphor of the mind as a chain of causes and effects. Both metaphors are to be found regularly in theories of psychological determinism.

There is also here a point that Bentham's critics have made much of: his apparent confusion of the 'ought' and the 'is' in deciding. If 'pleasure and pain' in fact determine how decisions are made, what sense can there be in saying that they 'ought' to do so? It is instructive, however, to see how Bentham escapes this difficulty—or at any rate avoids having to face it. The fact is that his is not a thorough-going psychological determinism. When he shifts from human motives to human reason, without being explicit about the point, he shifts from a context in which events happen *to* a man (in the manner of the world machine) to a context in which a man decides what he will do.

> Pleasures then, and the avoidance of pains, are the ends which the legislator has in view: it behoves him therefore to understand their value. Pleasures and pains are the instruments he has to work with: it behoves him therefore to understand their force, which is again, in other words, their value (ibid., pp. 802–803).

There is a similar contrast in Hume. When he speaks of 'appetites', he talks of motives and impulses which 'engage' man. But reason,

> . . . being cool and disengaged, is no motive to action, and directs only the impulse received from appetite or inclination, by showing us the means of attaining happiness or avoiding misery (Melden, ed., 1939, p. 285).

Hume and Bentham differ in their theories of mind, but they share this: as they shift from motives to reason they shift in their underlying metaphor from mechanism to deliberate human action. This suggests that the metaphor of the machine is directly related to the assumption of psychological determinism. The resulting model of the mind is very much like Ryle's 'ghost in the machine'. It is, perhaps more accurately, a little man directing or directed by a machine. The shift from mechanical to deliberate metaphor is nowhere justified in Bentham or Hume, but it makes plausible a shift from psychological determinism, which is tolerable enough when applied to impulses, to psychological indeterminism when the talk is of reason. A consistently determinist view of the mind—a determinism of reason as well as of impulse—would have been as uncongenial to Hume or Bentham as it is today to Stevenson.

Stevenson also writes in the metaphor of the machine when he speaks of attitudes and inclinations. He quotes Spinoza at his most mechanistic,

'An affect cannot be restrained or removed unless by an opposed and stronger affect' (Stevenson, 1944, p. 115).

speaks of a belief which

. . . reinforces an attitude, or diminishes its strength . . . (ibid., p. 115).

and talks about,

. . . the resultant effect on attitudes of a great number of beliefs (ibid., p. 130).

. . . attitude . . . reinforced by many others . . . (ibid., p. 131).

and uses words like 'pressing', 'fortifying', 'inhibiting', and 'springing'.

But there is also a shift both to anthropomorphic language and to indeterminism when Stevenson comes to speak of reason, or the formation of beliefs. For Stevenson this has its convenience. He is committed to a partial irrationalism in deciding—holding that not all conflicts of attitude will be resolvable by reason—but he wants to avoid the complete irrationalism which would result if the formation of beliefs were also an 'emotive' process. The shift from mechanical to deliberate metaphor allows him to appear to have his cake and eat it too.

This suggests the intriguing possibility that determinists and irrationalists in ethics are thinking in terms of a displaced theory of the machine, while indeterminists and rationalists are guided by the metaphor of deliberate action.

It is hard to say in the case of Hume, Bentham, and Stevenson whether a displaced theory of the mind as machine leads to the determinist view of impulse, or whether the determinist view is serviced by the displaced theory of the machine. It is pretty clear that the displacement of machine theory is implicit and undefended. It meshes with and promotes the determinist view of 'appetite'. It may also be that a metaphor which did not promote it would be rejected. The tendency to machine theory of mind and the tendency to psychological determinism appear to interact with and support one another.

There are several other kinds of assumption related to the determinism associated with the machine theory of mind.

One has to do with the perennial 'mind-body' problem which began in the seventeenth century to plague philosophers in a new form. If, with Descartes, we take the body to be a kind of geometrical machine and the mind, 'extensionless thought', it is difficult if not impossible to see how what happens in the mind can have any effect on the body, as it is supposed to have, particularly in an act of will. The theory of the machine, displaced to mental events, provides an apparent escape. When we say, with Bentham, that one 'motive', by 'joining forces' with another, causes a man to 'engage' in an action, we notice no leap from a mental to a physical world. A play of 'internal forces' results in an 'external action' just as the internal movement of an engine causes a car to move and to engage with another car. Thanks to the metaphor of the mind as an internal machine interacting with an external one—a metaphorical view whose literal application to the mind Bentham could vigorously deny—the problem of the will appears to evaporate.

A second assumption has to do with the mechanist treatment of 'principles'. In Newtonian mechanics 'forces', such as inertia and gravity, are often called 'principles'. This use of the term goes far back in the history of theories of the world—at least as far as the early Greek 'dry', 'hot', 'wet', and 'cold' principles. When such talk is translated to the mind, however, special problems arise. Thus we find Bentham speaking of the 'force' of principles, of principles versus 'motives', and the like. Benevolence and cruelty, as well as utility, are spoken of from time to time as 'motives' and we know that for Bentham motives have 'force'. A principle becomes in effect a *motive* with *force*. This image has filtered down to the present. Philosophers explore the force of principles. They ask how a principle can be a motive for action, in a sense that is held to be distinct from their inquiry into its justification. But why attribute 'force' to principles? Such an inquiry is bound to be fruitless unless the underlying mechanical metaphor is recognized and the nature of the 'motive force' of a principle made explicit in ways that distinguish it from mechanics.

The Mind can be Quantified

The Newtonian world machine is made up of accelerated masses in space, all of which are subject in principle to quantitative assessment, to measurement. When their vectors are taken into account, these quantities are additive: two equal forces acting in the same direction on a mass act with a force twice as great as the force of one. Moreover, these quantities are *merely* additive—the resultant of forces acting on a mass is neither more nor less than the sum of their vectors. The addition of still another force will not change that resultant out of proportion to its quantity. In conflict of forces quantity is decisive: if two opposite forces are acting on a mass, the mass will move, other things being equal, in the direction of the greater force.

There is hardly need to show that Bentham makes corresponding assumptions about the mind. He is famous for them. His method of estimating the value of an action consists in 'summing up' the values of the pleasure and pain resulting from the act. He assumes everywhere that forces of motives are additive and only additive—for example.

... the strength of the temptation, in any case, after deducting the force of the social motives, is as the sum of the forces of the seducing, to the sum of the forces of the occasional tutelary motives (Burtt, ed., 1939, p. 840).

For Bentham, as for Spinoza and Stevenson and our present common sense, motives of greater force overcome motives of lesser force.

Bentham does not defend these assumptions, although his supporters have defended them since. What is meant by the 'force' of a motive, or the 'sum' of the force of motives, as distinct from a Newtonian force or sum of forces? Bentham neither asserts that motives have measurable force in the Newtonian sense nor does he attempt to explain their differences. In fact, he does not seem to have been aware of the problem.

Causal Atomism

In the Newtonian world machine, causality is atomistic. It is made up of discrete sequential events, like the links of a chain. Each link in the chain is directly attributable to the one preceding it as, in the familiar eighteenth-century example of billiards, the movement of a ball is directly caused by the impact of another.

Our own commonsensical theory of mind embodies similar assumptions. In the mind, one event leads to another. We say, 'One thought leads to another.' We speak of trains or chains of associations. Given an action or a decision, we are apt to look for 'the feeling' or 'the thought' which came before it and caused it. This tendency is carried to an extreme in the ethical views of Moritz Schlick, a member of the Vienna Circle, whose particular brand of psychological hedonism envisions the life of the mind as a chain of thought and feelings in which decisions are determined by the hedonic content (pleasurable or painful) of the last preceding thought.

But why assume that the relation of cause and effect can hold only between proximate members of a chain of thoughts? Where is the evidence for these isolated thought entities coming one after another? What about horizontal relations to co-existing states of mind? It has been pointed out, moreover (in an unpublished paper by Dr Sol Levy), that this view of causality in the mind makes of every causal relation a little miracle. In each causal atom there is no basis for the succeeding effect, nothing that makes the effect coming out of it understandable. When causal events are conceived as discrete, atomic entities, there is no basis for their connection except what Hume called their constant conjunction. And the conjunction itself is always arbitrary. It is given rather than understood.

The metaphor of the causal chain is misleading in that there are, in time, no 'links': when material objects are conceived as discrete, their connection can still be understood along the lines of mechanical models. When temporal events are made discrete, their connections become mysterious. This mystery results from the spatialization of time and, more specifically, from the mechanical atomic model of temporal events. It sets the stage for one familiar form of the problem of induction—'How can it be established that observed past conjunctions of events will hold for the future?' And it makes for the obscurity underlying the doctrine of the association of ideas.

In Bentham, an author whose views consistently reflect the various facets of the mind as machine, there is a similar set of assumptions and a remarkable device for offering to avoid their obscurity. Bentham refers to 'chains of cause and effect' and 'chains of motives'.

> A fire breaks out in your neighbour's house; you are under apprehension of its extending to your own; you are apprehensive that if you stay in it, you will be burnt; you accordingly run out of it. This then is the act; all the others are motives to it.
>
> In all this chain of motives, the principle or original link seems to be the last internal motive in prospect: it is to this that all the other motives in prospect owe their materiality, and the immediately acting motive its existence (Burtt, ed., 1939, pp. 814–815).

Here motives leading up to an act function as a series of discrete temporal events. In this passage 'last' and 'immediate' are certainly temporal terms. But the series of discrete temporal events is also, minus a premise, a practical syllogism. It is a chain of propositions, which are 'first' or 'last' in the sense that some may be inferred from others.

Bentham is engaged in converting the temporal series to a logical one. The idea of a chain of mental events is part of what allows him to do this. The role of the isolated self-contained mental event—a kind of event one might seek in vain in the mind —is filled by the isolated self-contained proposition. And the temporal causal order of events in the mind is a translation of the logical order of the practical syllogism. In a way reminiscent of the other examples in which an underlying metaphor lends plausibility to a paradox, the highly paradoxical 'causal' order of mental events is made to seem plausible. The logical connection replaces the temporal miracle. There is no defence of this identification of propositions with motives and of logical with temporal orders. Bentham seems to be unaware of his own stratagem and of the means by which he accomplishes it—the by now familiar substitution of the justification of an act for its genesis. The very unconsciousness of the stratagem serves to highlight the causal atomism it was designed to counteract.

These three families of assumptions—determinism, the quantitative view of mind, and causal atomism—by no means exhaust the possible list. Much could be said, for example, about the role of static 'topographical' elements (the unchanging framework in which movement happens) both in the world machine and in the machine view of mind. Nevertheless, this limited set of assumptions indicates the power of the Newtonian machine as we, along with Bentham, Spinoza, Hume, and Stevenson, displace it to theories of mind. While each of these families of assumptions can be related in part to other metaphors and other tendencies, the Newtonian machine helps to point out and account for them all.

Although in the realm of physics the Newtonian machine has suffered reverses, it is still dominant in theories of mind. Never since the age of naïve metaphysical mechanism have we been so close to literal belief in the theory of mind as machine. We have seen the birth of the giant computers. From the beginning these machines were understood in terms of mental functions—perception, reasoning, learning, and memory; but it is becoming more and more common to think of the mind and mental processes in terms of computer behaviour. 'Information storage', 'information retrieval', 'input-output', 'circuit', 'read-out', 'digital and analogue', and similar computer-based terms, have gained in currency as ways of talking about thinking, learning, and reasoning. A new science, cybernetics, has grown up to explore the metaphor of mind as computer. The metaphor has been evocative and fruitful. It becomes dangerous only as it begins to go underground.

The view of the mind as computer is only one expression of the central metaphor of the machine in our culture. A generation ago Thorstein Veblen, in *The Theory of the Business Enterprise*, was already calling attention to it. His phrase is 'the machine process':

> In its bearing on modern life and modern business, the 'machine process' means something more comprehensive and less external than a mere aggregate of mechanical appliances for the mediation of human labour. It means that, but it means something more than that. . . . The sequence of the process involves both . . . the apparatus and the materials, in such intimate interaction that the process cannot be spoken of simply as an action of the apparatus upon the materials. . . .
>
> Wherever manual dexterity, the rule of thumb, and the fortuitous conjunctures of the seasons have been supplanted by a reasoned procedure on the basis of the systematic knowledge of the forces employed, there the mechanical industry is to be found, even in the absence of intricate mechanical contrivances (Veblen, 1923, pp. 5–6).

Veblen goes on to show how the demands of the machine process have affected social processes—how requirements for mechanical accuracy and adaptation to specific uses have led to standardization of the products and materials of industry, including human labour.

What he presents is the picture of a society in which nearly all major institutions are as though they had been made on the metaphor of the machine:

> . . . the modern means of *communication* and the system into which these means are organized are also of the nature of a mechanical process, and in this mechanical process of service and intercourse, the life of all civilized men is more or less intimately involved (ibid., 1923, p. 13).

> . . . *the modern industrial system* at large bears the character of a comprehensive, balanced mechanical process. . . . This mechanical concatenation of industrial processes makes for solidarity in the administration of any group of related industries, and more remotely it makes for solidarity in the management of the entire industrial traffic of the community (ibid., pp. 16–17).

But it is not entirely clear in Veblen how the machine process, in production, leads to mechanization of major social institutions. He shows to some extent the 'concatenation of processes' whereby mechanization arises to meet the demands of the machine. But there are leaps. He talks, for example, of the mechanization of morality and metaphysics:

> The discipline of the machine process enforces a standardization of conduct and of knowledge in terms of quantitative precision, and inculcates a habit of apprehending and explaining facts in terms of material cause and effect. It involves a valuation of facts, things, relations, and even personal capacity, in terms of force. Its metaphysics is materialism and its point of view is causal sequence (ibid., pp. 66–67).

Anyone who has lived in industry, and heard men treated regularly in terms of 'drive', 'forcefulness', 'sparking plugs', 'brakes', 'shifting of gears', 'self-starters', 'cogs in the machine', and the like, cannot help but admit some of the truth of this. But can we explain the growth of mechanized institutions and theories as Veblen wishes to explain it, merely by their usefulness to the working of an industrial society?

Such a habit of mind conduces to industrial efficiency, and the wide prevalence of such a habit is indispensable to a high degree of industrial efficiency under modern conditions. This habit of mind prevails most widely and with least faltering in those communities that have achieved great things in the machine industry, being both a cause and an effect of the machine process (ibid., p. 67).

Even if these theories and institutions are indispensable to the efficiency of the industrial process and are somehow 'selected' on this basis, how did they arise in the first place? They must have come to be in order to be selected.

Not surprisingly, it seems to me they can be understood as we have come to understand machine theories of mind. They are products of a dominant, prestigeful theory, the theory of the machine, which has influenced our culture not only directly by demands placed on institutions, but indirectly as a projective model for new theories.

DYNAMISM

Sullivan, in the passage quoted earlier, speaks of dynamisms as:

> ... processes [which are] very apt to go on until something in the way of a goal, a terminal state, is reached, whereupon they cease for the time being and show no trace until they are next called forth (Sullivan, 1956, p. 5).

Kurt Lewin has a similar passage in his *Dynamic Theory of Personality*.

> ... the forces which control the course of the process remain without effect or simply do not arise when no psychical energies are present, when there exists no connection with tense psychical systems which keep the process in motion (Lewin, 1935, pp. 50–51).

These forces are different from Newtonian forces. Although Lewin and Sullivan use words like 'force'—and 'balance', 'order', 'system' and 'motion'—they use them differently. Moreover, they use such additional terms as 'dynamic', 'field', and 'energy'. This different sort of usage pervades the writings of Gestalt psychologists like Köhler and Koffka; dynamic social theorists like Lewin; and dynamic psychiatric theorists like Sullivan, Horney, and Fromm-Reichmann.

These writers have displaced to the mind the dynamic field physics of the late nineteenth and early twentieth centuries. In them the physics of Maxwell has replaced the Newtonian machine. In Newtonian mechanics,

> . . . we discover the problem of physical material science to refer natural phenomena back to unchangeable attractive and repulsive forces whose intensity depends wholly upon distance (Einstein & Infeld, 1938, p. 58).

In Maxwellian field theory,

> . . . if we know the field at one instant only, we can deduce from the equations of the theory how the whole field will change in space and time. . . .
>
> In Maxwell's theory there are no material actors. The mathematical equations of this theory express the laws governing the electromagnetic field. They do not, as in Newton's laws, connect two widely separated events; they do not connect the happenings *here* with the conditions *there*. The field *here* and *now* depends on the field in the *immediate neighbourhood* at a time *just past*. . . . We can deduce what happens here from that which happened far away by the summation of these very small steps. In Newton's theory, on the contrary, only big steps connecting distinct events are permissible (ibid., p. 152).

Field theory, whether it be applied to gravitational force or to electromagnetism, includes the following:

(i) The major unit is no longer a mass, a particle, but a field of force—an area characterized by a particular distribution of lines of force.

(ii) Other things within the field are characterized by and determined by the field. They are best understood as properties of the field.

(iii) The field as a whole is viewed as constantly changing, each state of the whole determining the next state. Changes in the field are constantly changing distributions of forces as they affect things within the field. Conversely, the motion of things within the field affects the character of the field as a whole.

As compared to the Newtonian machine, far greater emphasis is placed here on the interdependence and changeability of phenomena.

The displacement of dynamic field physics does not seem to have made much headway yet in commonsense theories of mind. In order to see its influence, attention must be paid to formal theory where dynamic and mechanistic theories of mind can be compared. For our purposes it will be particularly useful to compare treatments of 'conflict of motives' in Bentham and in Kurt Lewin.

Since we have already said a good deal about Bentham, we will quote first from Lewin. The following passages are drawn from 'Environmental Forces in Child Behavior and Development', Chapter Three of *A Dynamic Theory of Personality*.

> The first presupposition for the understanding of the child is the determination of the psychological place at which the child concerned is and of his region of freedom of movement, that is, of the regions that are accessible to him and of those regions . . . to him. . . .
>
> One can characterize these possible and not possible psychodynamic locomotions (quasi-bodily, quasi-social, and quasi-mental locomotions) at every point of the environment. . . . The region which a child cannot reach one can characterize by means of barriers between these regions and their neighbouring regions. . . .
>
> To determine not only which locomotions (paths) are

possible but which of the possible locomotions will occur at a given moment one has to use the concept of force.

A force is defined through three properties: (1) direction, (2) strength, and (3) point of application. The first and second properties are to be represented through the mathematical concept vector. . . . The real locomotion must occur in every case according to the direction and the strength of the resultant of the momentary forces. . . .

The direction which the valence imparts to the child's behavior varies extremely, according to the content of the wants and needs. Nevertheless, one may distinguish two large groups of valences according to the sort of initial behavior they elicit: the positive valences (+), those effecting approach; and the negative (−), those producing withdrawal or retreat.

The actions in the direction of the valence may have the form of uncontrolled impulsive behavior or of directed voluntary activity. . . .

One has to distinguish between driving forces, which correspond to positive or negative valences, and restraining forces, which correspond to barriers.

That the valence is not associated merely with a subjective experience of direction, but that a directed force, determinative of the behavior, must be ascribed to it, may be seen in the fact that a change in the position of the attractive object brings about (other things being equal) a change in the direction of the child's movements.

The ways in which different valences may interact in a situation are naturally very numerous. . . .

Conflict is defined psychologically as the opposition of approximately equally strong field forces. There are three basic cases of conflict, so far as driving forces are concerned.

1. The child stands between two positive valences. . . .
2. The child faces something that has simultaneously both a positive and a negative valence. . . .
3. The third type of conflict situation occurs when the child

stands between two negative valences. . . (Lewin, 1935, pp. 80–91).

Before commenting on these passages, it will be helpful to recall a passage already quoted in Bentham:

> When a man has it in contemplation to engage in any action he is frequently acted upon at the same time by the force of divers motives: one motive, or set of motives, acting in one direction; another motive, or set of motives, acting as it were in the opposite direction. The motives on one side disposing him to engage in the action: those on the other disposing him not to engage in it. Now, any motive, the influence of which tends to dispose him to engage in the action in question, may be termed an impelling motive: any motive, the influence of which tends to dispose him not to engage in it, a restraining motive (Burtt, ed., 1939, pp. 831–832).

These passages are drawn from radically different contexts. Both writers are, in a sense, working out theories of human behaviour. But Bentham is specifically concerned here with presenting a normative code of conduct. In his discussion of conflict of motives, he wants to show that, since any motive may sanction any act, the goodness or badness of motives does not provide the basis for a code of conduct.

In the light of this, it is striking how much the two passages have in common. If 'child' replaced 'man' in Bentham's passage, it would not be terribly surprising—in spite of the fact that it was written about 150 years earlier—to find it in the middle of a page by Lewin. Attention to underlying metaphors compresses intellectual time.

Still, there are a number of significant differences. Bentham is thinking in terms of a Newtonian machine, like a car on a track pushed in opposite directions. Lewin, on the other hand, seems to be treating a child as a kind of charged particle in a Maxwellian field of electromagnetic force. The question is, what specific conceptual differences can be found?

The Conservative Function

1. What is viewed as conflicting?

For Bentham and Lewin alike conflict is 'an opposition of forces' but for Bentham these forces are 'motives' or 'inclinations' like 'benevolence' or 'self-regard', while for Lewin they are 'valences' or 'field forces'. For Bentham they are entities inside the man while for Lewin they are properties of aspects of the situation —for example, the property of a tree the child is trying to climb.

2. Where do the forces come from?

As Bentham treats them, they are apparently carried, in a potential state, by the man himself. They are brought to act on the man through the intermediary of his beliefs (which cause them to 'engage' with an act) on the occasion of his 'having it in contemplation to engage in an action'.

For Lewin, on the other hand, they come from the total situation—the child in the 'field'. The child does not bring them to the field. They are brought about by the forming and changing of the situation.

3. How permanent and independent are they?

Benevolence is benevolence. Self-regard is self-regard. For Bentham such forces may or may not act in a given process of practical reason, but they stay the same throughout a given process and from process to process regardless of what else is present. Although they may cause a man to change his mind or his action, they themselves are static and self-contained.

For Lewin, on the other hand, the forces of a situation are momentary forces. They may emerge suddenly and disappear suddenly.

> ... after the child has run against the barrier several times and perhaps hurt himself, or had the wounding experience of failure, the barrier itself acquires a negative valence. Beside the positive, there comes into existence a negative vector ...
> (Lewin, 1935, p. 89).

Their strength and their character change throughout the
160

process in response to what is happening elsewhere in the field.

For the strength of the valences, internal factors, especially the actual momentary state of the child's needs, are of crucial significance. In addition, the strength of the field force going out from a valence depends also upon the position of the valence relative to the individual and upon the presence or absence of other valences (ibid., p. 85).

4. What are the boundaries of the conflict and the kinds of responses that can be made to it?

Bentham always treats a conflict as consisting of two parts or sets of parts. These forces are always totally opposed or totally compatible. They influence a man with respect to a given contemplated act, and response to them takes the form of a decision for or against that act.

Lewin also tends to present conflict in twos:

He [the child] has to choose perhaps between going on a picnic and playing with his comrades (ibid., p. 89).

But in theory, at any rate, he allows for the possibility that a number of forces, of different direction, can act on the child in conflicting ways. His forces are sometimes directed at different objects in the field, rather than at a single act. Conflict is not an all-or-none affair; forces may be more or less opposed; conflicts may be more or less intense, more or less direct. Moreover, situations permit a wide variety of responses to conflict. 'The real locomotion must occur in every case according to the direction and strength of the resultant of the momentary forces.' But this 'locomotion' may take the form of moving towards or away from the 'valenced' object, moving to a 'point of equilibrium', 'withdrawing from the field', or the like.

Perhaps most important, Lewin does not view the situation— 'a man or child poised between action or inaction'—as remaining the same throughout the process. Each move made by the child changes the situation, and with a change in situation the momentary forces of the field also change. The nature of a conflict changes radically as responses to it are made. For Bentham, on the other hand, a conflict between benevolence and self-regard remains a conflict between benevolence and self-regard until it is resolved.

We would expect such conceptual differences if Bentham were influenced by the displacement of the Newtonian machine and Lewin, by the displacement of dynamic field physics.

Lewin's account is a direct transposition of field theory. Opposing forces are viewed as aspects of fields of force, determined by those fields and without identity apart from them. The field is in constant flux, each state determined by the preceding state of the whole, and therefore, individual forces within the field are constantly changing, too.

For Bentham, the opposing forces are entities in their own right, independent and relatively unchanging, like the 'unchangeable attractive and repulsive forces' of Newtonian mechanics.

Lewin's Awareness of his Analogies

Lewin shares with Gestalt psychologists the degree to which he appears to be aware of his own underlying metaphors:

> Thus in the psychological fields most fundamental to the whole behavior of living things the transition seems inevitable to a Galileian view of dynamics, which derives all its vectors not from single isolated objects, but from the mutual relations of the factors in the concrete whole situation, that is, essentially, from the momentary condition of the individual and the structure of the psychological situation (ibid., p. 41).

But this awareness is of a curiously intermittent character. Lewin seems to oscillate between the notion that he is offering a general theory, which includes as instances both physics and psychology, and the notion that he is treating psychological things in terms of the metaphor of physics.

> When the concept of energy is used here and when later those of force, of tension, of systems, and others are employed, the

question may be left quite open as to whether or not one should ultimately go back to physical forces and energies. In any event, these concepts are, in my opinion, general logical fundamental concepts of all dynamics (even though their treatment in logic is usually very much neglected). They are in no way a special possession of physics but are seen, for example, in economics . . . without requiring the assumption that therefore one must derive economics in some way from physics.

Quite independently, then, of [this question] . . . the treatment of causal dynamic problems compels psychology to employ the fundamental concepts of dynamics. . . . Physical analogies may often be drawn without damage to clarification. On the other hand, it is always necessary carefully to avoid certain very easy errors . . . and it must always be kept in mind that we have to do with forces in a *psychical* field and not in the physical environment (ibid., p. 46).

Since Lewin makes a distinction between 'physical analogies' and terms like 'force', 'tension', and the like, he apparently believes here that he is using these terms in a literal, *non*-analogical way. But when it comes down to it, it is not at all clear that this is what he does. He often points out that there *is* a difference between the application of a term in mechanics, and his application of it.

This is, to be sure, not equivalent to saying that we have here to do with a 'release' in the sense of the function of the spark in the cartridge or the driving rod in the steam engine (ibid., p. 47).

But he does not tell us what that difference is—and he continues to use the word drawn from mechanics.

His passages on 'environmental forces' in child behaviour are particularly instructive here. He uses examples which do involve the physical movement of masses in space—the movement of children. But he insists that terms like 'space', 'locomotion', 'force', 'vector', and 'field', are *not* meant in their merely physical sense. For example,

> . . . direction in the psychobiological field is not necessarily to be identified with physical direction, but must be defined primarily in the psychological terms (ibid., p. 84).

> . . . one may not . . . simply assume that psychological distance corresponds to physical distance (ibid., p. 86).

But he never does tell us what the non-mechanical senses of 'direction' and 'distance' are. For the most part, he leaves us to shift for ourselves—to understand metaphorically or to elaborate our own non-mechanical conceptual framework—on the basis of his examples. When he does attempt an explication of a mechanical term, it is through other terms also derived from the mechanical metaphor:

> A force is defined through three properties: (1) direction, (2) strength, and (3) point of application . . . (ibid, p. 81).

I would propose then, that Lewin is not presenting a general theory of dynamics, of which physics and psychology are instances, but a psychological theory based in part on the displacement of Maxwellian field physics. This does not detract from the liberating contributions he has made to psychological theory; but it distinguishes what he has done from what he seems to think he has done.

ATOMISM

I would like to touch somewhat more briefly on another kind of physical theory which has been displaced, with great consequence, to theories of mind.

Atomism arose long before the development of the Newtonian machine. In pre-Socratic Greece,

> The Atomists [Democritus and Leucippus] taught that everything happens by a cause and of necessity. They carried farther the Ionian attempt to explain matter in terms of simpler elements. Their atoms are identical in substance, but many in

size and shape; 'strong in solid singleness', they have existed and will exist for ever. Thus difference in the properties of bodies is due to differences in size, shape, and movement of atoms (Dampier, 1944, pp. 17–18).

In *De Rerum Natura* Lucretius carried on their tradition. His atomism depended on the following theorems:

Nature resolves everything into its component atoms and never reduces anything to nothing.
Material objects are of two kinds, atoms and compounds of atoms. The atoms themselves cannot be destroyed by any force for they are preserved indefinitely by their absolute solidity. The number of atoms of different forms is infinite.
It must not be supposed that atoms of every sort can be linked in every variety of combination (Bailey, ed., 1947).

However, after the emergence of the Newtonian machine, atomism took on the colouring of a Newtonian mechanical system. Atoms tended to be conceived as billiard-ball-like entities, with masses and accelerations, subject to Newtonian forces of attraction and repulsion. This was the sort of atomism which became in Dalton's theory the basis of nineteenth-century chemistry. Dalton's atomism was based on, and designed to explain, the facts of chemical combination in equivalent weights:

(i)   Each element is composed of ultimate indivisible particles or atoms.
(ii) All the atoms of any one element are identical. The atoms of no two elements are the same.
(iii) Compounds are formed by a definite number of atoms of one kind of element combining with a definite number of atoms of another kind of element to form molecules.

It will be news to no one, I think, that the psychological theories of the associationists—Hartley, Locke, Berkeley, Hume, and their descendants—represent the displacement of physical atomism. The term 'atomism' has come into common usage to describe such theories. But this relationship is not generally conceived in the context of an attempt to understand the displacement of theories. Moreover, the 'association of ideas' in its contemporary informal version—our everyday unthinking response to questions about memory, learning, and the like—is not usually related to its source in physical theory.

The British associationists set themselves the task of explaining all mental phenomena. The atomic theory came readily to hand, and they were able to adapt it neatly to their task. Consider Locke's discussion of 'complex ideas' in his *Concerning Human Understanding.*

> . . . We have hitherto considered those ideas, in the reception whereof the mind is only passive, which are those simple ones received from sensation and reflection before mentioned, whereof the mind cannot make one to itself, nor have any ideas which does not wholly consist of them. . . . The acts of the mind wherein it exerts its power over its simple ideas are chiefly these three: (1) Combining several simple ideas into one compound one; and thus all complex ideas are made. (2) The second is bringing two ideas, whether simple or complex, together, and setting them by one another, so as to take a view of them all at once, without uniting them into one; by which it gets all its ideas of relations. (3) The third is separating them from all other ideas that accompany them in their real existence; this is called abstraction; and thus all general ideas are made (Burtt, ed., 1939, p. 283).

Similar principles are to be found in Hume's *Enquiry Concerning Human Understanding:*

> It is evident that there is a principle of connection between the different thoughts or ideas of the mind, and that, in their appearance to the memory or imagination, they introduce each other with a certain degree of method and regularity . . . the simple ideas, comprehended in the compound ones, were bound together by some universal principle, which had an

equal influence on all mankind. . . . To me, there appear to be only three principles of connection among ideas, namely Resemblance, Contiguity in time or place, and Cause or Effect (ibid., pp. 596–597).

The mind is presented here as a sort of enclosed place in which simple, solid things—'ideas'—are produced by impressions from the outside world. The kinds of simple ideas are few in number and unchanging. All change in the mind is due to the regular, lawlike interaction of these ideas which combine with one another according to definite laws to form 'complexes'. The programme of associationism was the progressive explanation of all the contents and processes of mind—perception, memory, imagination, reasoning, etc.—in terms of these theorems. As British empiricism proceeded towards Berkeleian idealism—reducing qualities of 'things in themselves' to aspects of mind—the associationist programme became in effect the programme of philosophy.

When we read Locke and Hume we seem to find great simplicity and obviousness. This is because British associationists have so thoroughly influenced what we now take to be common sense. Our own answers to hard questions about the mind come out almost automatically in their terms.

What is there in the mind? *Ideas.*
How do they get into the mind? *From the world, through the senses.*
How do we remember things? *Ideas get to be associated with one another when they occur together. One idea is able to call up another with which it has been associated.*
What is thinking? *It consists in a 'train of thoughts', or in 'putting our ideas in order'.*

With this view of mind, our common sense stands in a historical current of thought. Atomistic theory of mind can be traced back to Aristotle, who had his own notion of the association of ideas, and forward to some contemporary psychologies which seek to understand thinking as the lawlike combination and recombination of isolated 'bits' of information, on the model of computers.

To the extent that the British associationists were aware of their debt to atomic theory, they denied its metaphorical influence. On the contrary, they presented their psychology as a literal application of the theory:

> This [the treatment of complex ideas] shows man's power and its way of operation to be much the same in the material and intellectual world. For, the materials in both being such as he has no power over, either to make or destroy, all that man can do is either to unite them together, or to set them by one another, or wholly separate them (Burtt, ed., 1939, p. 283).

The obviousness of this application fades immediately, however, when it is noticed that the mind, in the associationists' own terms, is not a space. On the contrary, space and its various aspects are taken to represent one family of ideas in the mind. What meaning can be given, then, to terms like 'combining ideas', 'bringing two ideas together and setting them by one another', 'separating ideas', 'ideas bound together', 'connections of ideas'? These terms refer to our experience of the spatial world. Can ideas be 'separated' or 'set by one another' if not in space?

The theory is either absurd, or else it is metaphorical—that is, it represents a displaced theory of the interaction of atoms in space. The main theorems of associationism can be seen, then, as direct transpositions of physical atomism:

(i) The contents of the mind are reducible to simple, indivisible ideas.

(ii) Every object of awareness is either such a simple idea, or an idea, compounded according to certain laws, out of simples.

It is characteristically unclear in the writings of the associationists whether these theorems are intended as assumptions or as propositions to be proved. Hume embarks on a proof of (ii),

> To prove this, the following two arguments will, I hope, be sufficient. First, when we analyze our thoughts or ideas, how-

ever compounded or sublime, we always find that they resolve themselves into such simple ideas as were copies from a precedent feeling or sentiment (ibid., p. 594).

But the arguments turn out to aim at proving that ideas are derived from 'impressions', not that ideas (or for that matter impressions) are 'simple'. Most often the theorems are defended by appeal to 'experience'. But this 'experience' is already infused with the very assumptions to be proved.

It is a mark of the influence of associationism that, in the last two centuries, virtually every new theory of mind has had to begin with a critique of associationist principles. However, this has not prevented these principles from lodging comfortably in the nest of common sense. Perhaps for this reason, the critique goes on. Contemporary philosophical criticism, for example, has tended to show that the associationists confused logical and genetic 'origins' of ideas. Contemporary psychological criticism has tended to aim at showing up assumptions underlying the 'experience' to which the associationists appealed.

Both psychologists and philosophers have attacked the root notion of 'simplicity'. Just as the simplicity of the physical atom had been dissolved in the nineteenth and twentieth centuries so, at a lag, has the transposed simplicity of the psychological atom. Ideas like 'red', 'smooth', 'large', 'pain'—the atomic stock-in-trade of the eighteenth-century associationists—have been exposed as rather sophisticated constructs imposed on experience by theories of the world. Sense-data theorists have tried to replace these naïve concepts with the more advanced 'primitive ideas' of 'red-patch-here', 'smoothness-there'—the evanescent phenomena of 'direct' perception. These theorists have had their own problems, and have been accused in turn of imposing their own 'constructs' on experience. The search for 'simples', and the attack on candidates for simplicity, has characterized nearly all areas of theories of mind. The logical atomists, like Carnap, have tried to establish the construction of simple primitive terms and sentences. Learning theorists and stimulus-response psychologists have proposed 'simple behaviours' in order to explain learning, perception, memory, and the like, by their combination. Pareto and his followers in the area of group behaviour have proposed 'simple interactions' as a basis for group theory. All of these 'simples' represent further displacements of physical atomism— and each in its turn has come under fire.

A Theory of Understanding: Vision

In Plato's famous myth of the cave, men are chained to the wall of a cave, able to see only the shadows they cast on the wall, not the fire behind them. Theirs is the shadowy world of sense perception, in which illusion cannot be distinguished from reality. Occasionally a man breaks his chains and makes his way out of the cave. There he sees the world of things, illuminated by the sun. Under the symbol of the perception of things, Plato is talking about perception of the forms or essences of things, the grasping of universals. If a man looks at the sun itself—the source of his vision of things—he is blinded. Its brilliance (the brilliance of the form of forms) is too much for him. If he returns to the cave again, to the shadowy world of men, he is blinded at first and cannot communicate his vision of things to men who see only shadows.

This familiar myth treats knowledge, understanding, learning, discovery, in terms of vision. Plato based his theory of knowledge on the metaphor of vision, in which he may have resembled the common sense of his time and certainly resembles the common sense of ours. Our concepts of understanding and discovery rest on a displaced theory of seeing.

This displacement is reflected in the systematic ambiguity of language about understanding and discovery:

I *see* this.
I *see* what you mean.
I *see that* something is the case.

Similarly, we *perceive, recognize, discern, regard, make out, look for, scrutinize* . . . an idea, theory or argument.

Ideas are given visual properties. They are: *large, well formed, hazy, vague, solid, clear, bright, sharp, obscure, fuzzy, shadowy.*

Understanding is *bright* or *dim.*

Light is *brought to bear* on a subject; or again, we are *in the dark* about it. It has *aspects* or *views.*

A wise man is *enlightened.* He is a man of *insight* and *vision.*

We make *observations*; we are capable of *introspection* and *reflection.*

Discovery is characterized by *illumination, a flash of brilliance.* A solution *appears* to us.

These metaphors of vision have played central roles in our culture in every formal theory of truth and knowledge.

The medieval theories of *revelation* are a case in point. Truth is conceived here as a light revealed to man. The road to salvation, like the myth of the cave, is conceived as a passage from darkness to light. The divine light, like the light of the sun, cannot be produced by man. It can be sought for, prayed for, awaited. When it comes, illumination is sudden, and blinding. The saved are luminous. They carry an inner light.

In Descartes, and in seventeenth-century rationalism generally, the divine light becomes the natural light, the light of reason. Its exercise is intuition, and its result is the formation of 'clear and distinct ideas'.

In the subjects we propose to investigate, our inquiries should be directed, not to what others have thought, nor to what we ourselves conjecture, but to *what we can clearly and perspicuously behold and with certainty deduce;* for knowledge is not won in any other way (Eaton, ed., 1927, p. 44).

By *intuition*, I understand . . . the conception which an *unclouded* and attentive mind gives us so readily and *distinctly* that we are wholly freed from doubt about that which we understand. Or, what comes to the same thing, *intuition is the undoubting conception of an unclouded and attentive mind, and springs from the light of reason alone* (ibid., p. 46).

Everyone is familiar with concepts like the light of reason, intuition, and clear and distinct ideas, even though, from the seventeenth century on, there has been debate over their meaning. From the point of view of the displacement of concepts, it suggests itself that intuition is displaced seeing; the 'clarity and distinctness' of ideas is a displaced clarity of objects; and the light of reason is a displaced theory of the eye, the eye of the mind, containing covertly the ancient doctrine that the eye projects its own light.

From this source comes the obviousness of the notion that there is an inner faculty of perception capable of determining the truth simply by inspection.

... many things are known with certainty, though not by themselves evident, but only deduced from true and known principles by the continuous and uninterrupted action of a mind that has a *clear vision* of each step in the process (ibid., p. 47).

Descartes' rationalistic view that the truth about things can be ascertained by intuition and deduction, without inspection of the things themselves, derives most of its plausibility from a symbolic Empiricism—that is, from a displaced theory of vision.

Vision-based theories of understanding and discovery continue with vigour in our own time. The most widely held theories of understanding and discovery derive in part from Gestalt psychology which began with a theory of visual perception. Its theory of understanding is based on the metaphor of vision. This is implicit in its name: it is a theory of *form* and of the discerning of forms. One of its major concepts is *insight*, which it defines in terms of the sudden reorganization of perceptual fields. It is concerned with foreground and background, with the completion of forms, the organization of elements of a field, coming to 'see things in different ways'. Its stock-in-trade is the emergence of patterns.

Depth psychology and specifically psycho-analysis has grasped the concept of insight, clear vision into oneself, as central to its theory of understanding. When an analyst like Hutchinson offers a theory of discovery, it is full of terms like 'insight', 'reorganization of perceptual fields', 'revelation', 'flashes of light', and the like. Discovery is a flash of light illuminating objects that are dark, permitting them to be clearly seen.

The theory of vision underlying these theories of understanding is not the sophisticated optics of today. It is a simple-minded three-part theory of objects, light, and the eye. The objects are there, just as we see them. They impress themselves on the eye, by means of reflected light. Sometimes, the eye is treated as a kind of searchlight, casting its own light on objects.

In vision-based theories of understanding, ideas are objects of the mind. They are perceived in the light of the mind by the eye of the mind, thought or understanding. The mind is a kind of magic-lantern show, as in Hume's view of ideas as faint images of sensation. Thinking is then 'image-ination'.

It is not easy to get at the assumptions carried over with this displaced theory of vision, which may be a measure of the central and entrenched position of the metaphor. There is one particularly striking family of assumptions, however, all having to do with the independence and objectness of ideas. It is related to our disposition, often remarked by Wittgenstein, to treat ideas as things.

According to a naïve theory of seeing, the eye is passive towards the object seen. The eye is opened and, through reflected light, the object impresses itself upon it. In the model of the camera this passivity is heightened; the eye is a simple receptor. Similarly, our ordinary talk about understanding presents the mind as passive to ideas:

We see what is meant . . .
An idea *appears*, *seems* to us . . .
An idea is *envisioned* . . .

According to the naïve theory of vision, the eye does not contribute anything to the object seen; it simply registers the object. Similarly, when understanding is treated as a kind of seeing, the mind simply registers the idea.

Contrast with this a theory of understanding based on a displaced theory of touch. Touching is more apparently active. It involves reaching out, exploring.

I have a feeling for what you mean . . .
I begin to grasp what you mean . . .

These sentences convey a different relation to the meaning than 'I see what you mean'. Touching is conceived of as more constitutive of the object touched; we put more into it.

It follows from the supposed passivity of the eye that the object seen is wholly there, with all its *visual* properties, colour, shape, size. It exists prior to the act of seeing, and it is unaffected by the act of seeing. 'I see' is fundamentally different in this sense from 'I create', 'I form', 'I contribute to', 'I participate in'. On this view, 'I see a yellow flower' is simply a reference to the fact that there is a yellow flower out there (yellowness and all) and it is being registered on my eye.

Visual objects are treated as self-contained and, in all their concreteness, independent of the eye. When ideas are treated as visual objects, they too become self-contained and pre-existent. We say,

Here is an idea. Do you understand it?

What makes us think that there is anything there, fully formed, waiting to be understood? Why do we assume that it is there prior to the process of understanding, or that it will remain essentially what it is, unaffected by the process of understanding? We say,

This is my idea.
I have to get my ideas in order.

When we treat ideas in this way, they are a kind of mental furniture—things, with a solidity and identity of their own. We can play an active role with respect to them, just as we can with visual objects, but by and large they are what they are independent of us, and we simply apprehend them.

Similarly, visual objects are treated as independent of person. A tree is a tree, regardless of the person looking at it. In the ordinary course of things, I do not doubt that the egg on the plate looks any different to you than it does to me. Colour blindness is an aberration; it is ordinarily construed as a failure to see things the way they are. In vision-based theories of understanding ideas are viewed as being what they are, independent of person. We say,

What do you think of segregation?
Do you believe in the virgin birth?

and the assumption is that segregation and the virgin birth are what they are, regardless of the person considering them. The observation that 'People look at things differently', or 'It's all relative', is generally a piece of conventional insight, used to end arguments but ignored in the ordinary course of life.

Some of these assumptions come more sharply into focus when it is asked how understanding can be improved. If we do not see an object clearly, what can we do? We can clear our eyes, open them wider, or squint and gaze steadily; we can move so that the object is closer or less obscured by obstacles, glare, shadow, and the like; we can use a seeing aid of some kind; we can change the lighting. In short, the things we can change are the position of the receptor with respect to the object; the illumination; the adequacy of the receptor. Descartes' *Improvement of the Understanding* can be read as a nearly point-by-point transposition of this theory. The object of study is the formation of clear and distinct ideas. The way to get these is to move closer (break the idea into parts, and inspect the parts); to remove obstacles (clear the mind of other objects of attention); gaze steadily (subject the idea to sustained inspection); improve the eye (train the mind by education). It is interesting that there is no analogue to improvement of the lighting; according to the most naïve theory of vision, you do not see light—you see the object.

This view of improvement of the understanding has by no means disappeared. There is still a view of 'study' which would

175

have us gaze steadily at the idea to be understood, clearing the mind of distracting thoughts, and by 'concentrating' clearly apprehend it. What this view overlooks, among other things, is the role of experiment and active exploration (which Descartes practised but tended to ignore in his theory of knowledge); and the essential relatedness of ideas—that is, our ability to make sense of them only in terms of their context. It also assumes that either an idea is understood or it is not—just as an object is either clearly seen or not—rather than viewing understanding as a gradual and essentially open-ended process which is never done.

The vision-based theory of understanding states that direct inspection, or intuition, results in clear ideas, each of which is conceived individually and discretely (where clarity is sometimes identified with this discreteness). Understanding is an all-or-none affair. Ideas are formed and concrete, like things, prior to understanding; they are independent of person and of the act of understanding itself.

This theory is based on naïve realism and direct, passive sense-reception of objects. In some versions, it ignores the role of light as a medium or regards the light as thrown out by the eye itself. Long before Descartes this theory of vision had fallen into disrepute, but in its sheltered metaphorical role it has persisted to the present day. As theory of vision developed—giving a more active role to the eye and brain, making of perception a process partly constitutive of the object perceived—formal theories of understanding have changed as well, giving a more active role to the understanding and a less independent, self-sufficient, thing-like status to the objects of understanding. But this change has been at a lag. Common-sense theories of understanding are still based on common-sense theories of seeing.

A THEORY OF ROMANTIC LOVE

It seems strange to speak of a 'theory' of romantic love. And yet, in the informal sense of a way of looking at things, a series of
176

expectations that could be partly formulated in propositions, our language and behaviour suggest that we have a theory of romantic love just as we have a theory of understanding. Moreover, the theory has received formal expression in our culture which vision-based theories of understanding never attained, as witness the romantic love poetry of the nineteenth century and of the popular movies, novels, and songs of our own day. The theory is at once normative and descriptive: it tells what love is and prescribes articles of faith in love. Although its canons are seldom assembled in one place and distilled from surrounding material, in their pure form, they would look something like this:

1. Love is 'fated'. We cannot predict when it will strike. When it does, we are helpless. It is a force that carries us with it, even against our will.
2. It is stronger and more beautiful than ordinary happiness, society, or morality.
3. It promises a bliss beyond ordinary human joys.
4. It imposes the most stringent fidelity upon the lover.
5. It thrives on absence and obstacles; it withers with complete possession.
6. It is always adulterous; it is incompatible with the regular satisfactions and duties of marriage.
7. It is always tied to suffering. Its purest form is mortal love, which ends in death.

The last three themes—the need for absence, adultery, suffering and death—are apt to be ignored or denied. Yet they characterize the purest and most typical of our love stories. The most typical moving love story is the one in which the hero and heroine meet, fall in love, give each other a sign of love; are separated, yearn for each other, strive vainly to overcome obstacles to one another (usually associated with family, morality, and other conventional social values); suffer, remain faithful, and finally gain complete possession of one another only in death. Television series and the popular magazines are all regular purveyors of the myth.

In something like this sense, there have been many books about

177

romantic love. Two writers, particularly, have dealt with its cultural antecedents, both detailing what I would call the displacement of earlier theories, although neither focuses on the nature of the process of displacement. Both trace romantic love to feudalism and to aspects of medieval Christianity, relating them in metaphorical terms. They concentrate on different elements of romantic love and trace it to varying forms of Christianity.

These writers are C. S. Lewis (*The Allegory of Love*) and Denis de Rougemont (*Love in the Western World*). I will sketch the lines of development they describe, as examples of the displacement of theories, and then go on to discuss two other forms of theory that are traceable to displacement from a similar source.

C. S. Lewis begins with a view of romantic love not unlike the one just described. He points out that it is an invention utterly foreign to classical culture.

> It seems to us natural that love should be the commonest theme of serious imaginative literature: but a glance at classical antiquity or at the Dark Ages at once shows us that what we took for 'nature' is really a special state of affairs, which will probably have an end, and which certainly had a beginning in eleventh-century Provence. . . . French poets, in the eleventh century, discovered or invented, or were the first to express, that romantic species of passion which English poets were still writing about in the nineteenth (Lewis, 1958, pp. 3-4).

The invention, Lewis says, is the theory and practice of courtly love. He traces it to several theories current in medieval culture. One of these is the feudal system:

> There is a service of love closely modelled on the service which a feudal vassal owes to his lord. The lover is the lady's 'man'. He addresses her as *midons*, which etymologically represents not 'my lady' but 'my lord'. The whole attitude has been rightly described as a 'feudalization of love'. This solemn amatory ritual is felt to be part and parcel of the courtly life (ibid., p. 2).

178

Another source is medieval Christianity itself:

Finally we come to the fourth mark of courtly love—its love religion of the god Amor. This is partly, as we have seen, an inheritance from Ovid. In part it is due to that same law of transference which determined that all the emotion stored in the vassal's relation to his seigneur should attach itself to the new kind of love: the forms of religious emotion would naturally tend to get into the love poetry, for the same reason. But in part (and this is, perhaps, the most important reason of the three) this erotic religion arises as a rival or a parody of the real religion and emphasizes the antagonism of the two ideals (ibid., p. 18).

The nature of this religion Lewis expresses in the following way:

It is as if some lover's metaphor when he said 'Here is my heaven' in a moment of passionate abandonment were taken up and expanded into a system. Even while he speaks he knows that 'here' is not his real heaven; and yet it is a delightful audacity to develop the idea a little further. If you go on to add to that lover's 'heaven' its natural accessories, a god and saints and a list of commandments, and if you picture the lover praying, sinning, repenting, and finally admitted to bliss, you will find yourself in the precarious dream-world of medieval love poetry. An extension of religion, an escape from religion, a rival religion ... (ibid., p. 21).

Lewis does not develop this concept of the metaphorical relation between courtly love and Christianity. For him it is merely a pedagogical device. And yet it is clear that the theory of courtly love, as he develops it, is a transposition and interpretation of the elements of Christian theory. 'Saints', 'sins', 'prayer', 'God', 'repentance', are not the same in courtly love as in Christianity, but the courtly elements are related to one another in the manner of their Christian counterparts—which allows us to say that medieval Christianity served as a projective model for the development of the theory of courtly love.

Moreover, Lewis regards these feudal and religious sources as essentially inseparable.

> We find also [in Lancelot] the conception of lovers as the members of an *order* of Love, modelled upon the orders of religion: of an art of Love, as in Ovid; and of a *court* of Love, with solemn customs and usages, modelled upon the feudal courts of the period. It will be seen that no final distinction is possible between the erotic religion, the erotic allegory, and the erotic mythology (ibid., p. 32).

Having established the origins of courtly love in this way, Lewis goes on to present its flowering and waning in the writings of Chrétien de Troyes, the *Roman de la Rose*, the School of Chartres, Chaucer, the English followers of Chaucer, and finally in Spenser, in whom he finds a fellow historian of the process. Some of its milestones are the fusion of courtly and divine love (in Dante); the extension of courtly love to marriage (appropriately, in post-Chaucerian England); and the death of courtly love (in Spenser)—a death from which it was to re-emerge in its modern guise of romantic love.

The romantic love of Denis de Rougemont puts much greater emphasis on the elements of absence, suffering, and death—elements which Lewis remarks only in occasional quasi-Freudian references to 'masochism'. This leads de Rougemont, in *his* search for origins, to concentrate on other aspects both of courtly love and of the medieval Christianity from which it was derived. Like Lewis, de Rougemont finds the origins of romantic love in

> . . . the chivalry of the 12th and 13th centuries. As a matter of fact, this group has long since dissolved. However secretly and diffusely, its laws are still ours. Although they have been secularized and denied by our official codes, they have become all the more binding in that they have power only over our dreams (de Rougemont, 1956, p. 6).

For de Rougemont, however, the central myth of courtly love is the myth of Tristan and Isolde.

In the myth of Tristan, de Rougemont finds a number of paradoxes, all having to do with the lovers' tendency to avoid complete possession and to maintain chastity—in effect, to promote
their own downfall—even when no external obstacles are present. He explains the paradoxes by finding in Tristan a myth of
courtly love, one of whose central themes is,

> That is no longer love, which turns to reality (ibid., p. 23).

De Rougemont also finds courtly love to be a feudalization of
love: the lady replaces the feudal sovereign, but the relation to
the 'vassal' remains the same. And he finds in Tristan a conflict
between the 'religions' of courtly and feudal love, just as Lewis
found in his material a conflict of courtly and divine love.

But in the myth of Tristan, de Rougemont finds other things.
Tristan and Isolde do not initially love one another, but are
forced to one another by the philtre (their passionate destiny). In
order to burn with the love-flame, they need each other—but in
absence. To this end they seek out obstacles; and the search for
obstacles is, in the end, a search for death.

> In this way, the preference given to voluntary obstacles is an
> affirmation of death, a progress toward Death! But towards a
> love-death, a voluntary death at the end of a series of trials
> from which Tristan emerges purified; toward a death which is
> a transfiguration and not a brutal accident. . . . What they gain
> in dying of love is their destiny: it is their revenge on the
> philtre . . . and passion in the end plays the role of a purifying
> trial, one would almost say a trial of penitence in the service of
> a transfiguring death . . . (ibid., pp. 36–37).

De Rougemont takes up and expands the 'masochistic' element
of both romantic and courtly love, to which Lewis refers only
in passing.

But this means that de Rougemont cannot explain the emergence of courtly love from a Christianity like Lewis's. He turns
instead to heretical faith, and specifically to the Manichaean

heresy of the Cathars. The chief doctrines of the heresy were these:

> God is love. But the world is bad. Therefore God could not have been the author of the world, of its darkness, and of the sin which grips it. His first creation, still unformed, was completed but perverted by the rebellious Angel, Satan or the Demiurge. Man is a fallen angel, emprisoned in matter and subject therefore to the laws of the body, of which the most tyrannical is procreation. But the Son of God came to show us the way to return to the Light. This Christ was not an incarnation: he only took on the appearance of a man. . . . Triple heresy against the Trinity: it divided the Father, distinguishing God and Jehovah; it lessened the role of the Son by emptying the role of the Cross and the unique redemption; finally it exaggerated and denatured the role of the Holy Ghost . . . which it made into 'the Mother of God', the feminine principle of love . . . (ibid., pp. 75–76).

De Rougemont goes on to describe the ritual of *consolamentum*; the ritual kiss by which the faithful were admitted into spiritual life; the trials and fasts that constituted initiation; the mandatory chastity; the distinction between the elite of the faith (*perfecti*) and the simple believers; and finally the ritual progress of detachment from life and from material things, ending in ritual suicide—the rise of the prepared soul from the darkness of the world to the light of God.

Not surprisingly, he is able to find in the perverse courtly love of Tristan—with its idealization of the lady, its self-torment and self-imposed chastity, its progressive detachment from the morality and material happiness of the living, and its eventual unity of lover and beloved in death—a structure built on the model of the Manichaean heresy. He goes further. He presents evidence purporting to show that the Cathars, persecuted by the Church of Rome, went underground; became the *trouvères*—troubadours from the monasteries of Provence—who in their songs of courtly love symbolically preached and protected the Manichaean faith. He concludes:

1. that the passion currently vulgarized in novels and movies is nothing other than the overflow, the anarchical invasion of our lives by a mystical heresy to which we have lost the key.
2. that at the origins of our marriage crisis there is nothing less than the conflict of two religious traditions . . . (ibid., p. 119).

He goes on, then, to trace the progress of the displaced heretical theory through the doctrine of courtly love, the romanticism of Milton and Shakespeare, and finally the romanticism of the nineteenth century and its popularization in our own time.

Lewis and de Rougemont alike, beginning with the undefended assumptions of our informal and sometimes covert theory of romantic love, present a complex history of romantic love. Both trace it to the courtly love of eleventh-century Provence. Both trace this, in turn, to the feudalized religion of medieval times. In my terms, they explain it as a displacement of that religion. But de Rougemont, focusing on the perverse, death-seeking character of courtly love, selects as source of that displacement the Manichaean heresy of the Cathars.

The story of this displacement of medieval Christianity (or a-Christianity) to romantic love, is particularly important because of the role played in our culture by romantic love and the romantic lover. Not only have these become powerful and popular but they have served, in turn, as projective models for other roles. Specifically, the theory of the romantic lover was displaced, probably in the course of the nineteenth century, to the modern theories of the artist and the revolutionary. Artist and revolutionary represent versions of the romantic lover just as the romantic lover once grew up as a version of the religious mystic.

This line of descent—from mystic to courtly love, to romantic lover, to artist and revolutionary—is far from simple and clear, but it is striking, at least in outline, and it helps to explain much

183

that is puzzling (as well as half-hidden and undefended) in these crucial roles. I am speaking here, of course, about our *stereotypes* of the artist and the revolutionary—stereotypes which may correspond more or less to the reality but are in any case always active and imposing in their demands. That is to say, these stereotyped roles are waiting in our culture for men to fill them; they act as magnetic poles surrounded by fields of force, drawing towards them those with a certain 'charge', repelling others. An artist in America must swim against the tide to avoid becoming an Artist.

Since we are considering the hypothesis that the role of artist and revolutionary were formed on the projective model of the romantic lover, it will be necessary to consider the romantic lover in profile.

1. In order to play his role, he must move away from society

Tristan, when he accepts his tragic destiny, sails away from the kingdom of Marc in a rudderless boat, carrying only his sword and his harp. In a thousand novels and poems of love, the lover turns his back on society in order to pursue his love (which may or may not entail pursuit of his beloved). By definition, the revolutionary takes this posture. In countless prints from the romantic era, the artist is pictured as moving away from society. Our current notion of the artist as bohemian, non-conformist, beatnik, and apostate, fall in line.

2. He defines himself in opposition to society

The romantic lover is not incidentally removed from society: he defines himself by his move away from it. He embarks on his career of romantic love with a symbolic rejection of society and its gifts. Tristan is at war with Marc. A thousand romantic heroes and heroines begin their romantic careers with a symbolic rejection of home, family, convention, and morality. Tristan's gesture is repeated, centuries later, by Emma Bovary, Vronsky, and Anna, and, in miniature, by every adolescent inebriate of the popular romanticism of his day.

Again, the revolutionary is defined by his rejection of the

dominant social and political order. And, in our time, to become an artist is to make a similar gesture.

It is worth noticing here that the language of romantic love creeps into the theory of the revolutionary and the artist—art, as well as freedom and country, are harsh 'mistresses', always presented in feminine form, to whom the artist and revolutionary swear 'service'; they remain 'faithful' to them; they are pictured as being 'in love' with them. Moreover, the languages of art and revolution invade one another's province. We speak of 'revolutions in art' and of 'revolutionary artists'; and, conversely, we speak of the 'art of revolution'. The lines of displacement appear to move horizontally as well as vertically.

3. He is fated to his role; he has no choice; he is swept along, often against his will
Tristan drinks the philtre (which de Rougemont calls 'the alibi of passion') and falls into a compelling dream from which he awakens, in some versions, three years later. The classic romantic plea is, 'We could not help ourselves', or, vulgarly, 'This is bigger than both of us'.

Conventionally, the revolutionary is pictured as being held fast in the grip of an ideal or movement which he cannot resist. 'The fatherland calls. How can I say no?' The artist too, is presented as subject to a compelling call—like a religious vocation— which he is unable to resist. The romantic literature is full of stories of artists ruined and exalted by their compelling destinies. The test of the 'true artist' is often held to be his unswerving devotion to art, as though its hold on him were absolute. He is the man who will paint (write, sculpt, etc.) come what may (only, as Somerset Maugham has pointed out, the unswerving destiny may go hand in hand with lack of talent).

4. He seeks a bliss, through love, beyond the ordinary happiness associated with society and conventional success and morality
For Tristan it is the bliss of passion (not the bliss of possession); it is the intoxication which grips Vronsky and Anna in the first, luminous days of their affair. It is the 'swoon', 'black magic',

'intoxication', 'bliss', 'joy', of the one who is 'sent', 'gone', 'out of this world', in the popular songs. For the revolutionary it is the intoxication of devotion (and perhaps martyrdom) to the ascending cause. For the artist, it is the intoxication of inspiration—the 'hard gemlike flame' of a generation or two ago; it is the transport of creation.

5. *He is able to progress, to obey his destiny, only through suffering— which he must seek out if the external world does not provide it for him*
Tristan and Isolde, when they embark on their love, embark on a career of suffering. When they seem to have escaped suffering at the hands of Marc and his barons, they provide it for themselves (the naked sword between them in the forest). 'Ah, que je souffre!', is the classic cry of French romantic novels, transformed in the popular song to 'Oh, baby, you hurt me so!' It is a short step to the artistic imperative—'You must suffer!'—pronounced by the romantic poets of the nineteenth century, echoed by Stanislavsky, and parodied ever since. The suffering of the revolutionary martyr, in the manner of Dostoievsky, has been a standard part of the stories of all the revolutionary heroes—from Lenin, to Stalin, Mao Tse-tung, Castro, and Djilas. It is, in a sense, their ticket of admission; they would be suspect without it.

6. *He pursues an ideal, which demands of him the strictest fidelity— often without the slightest hope of reward*
This is the hallmark of the courtly lover's 'service' to his 'lady'. Tristan and Isolde pledge undying fidelity to one another, just at the moment when they are separated and relegated to their respective sterile marriages. 'Faithfulness till death' is the motto of the romantic lover—particularly when it must be upheld in the absence of the beloved. The artist's faithfulness to his ideals is treated in precisely the same way. It must always be asked of him, 'has he remained faithful?' or 'has he gone over?' The more painful and difficult the fidelity—as in the now-stereotyped cases of Van Gogh and Gauguin—the more glorious the career. The revolutionary's faithfulness is a matter of common parlance, and the obsession with fidelity among revolutionaries (reminiscent

of the orthodoxies and heterodoxies of the early Church) goes some way towards explaining for us the comic opera accusations and counter-accusations of revolutionary and counter-revolutionary affiliation which filter through the Iron and Bamboo Curtains.

7. Sustained consummation—complete possession—is disastrous
The marriage bell is the death knell of romantic love. (As de Rougemont points out, imagine the absurdity of Mrs Tristan!). Traditionally, the acquisition of power corrupts and perverts the revolutionary—he becomes inevitably now the target of the new revolutionary heroes of the romantic myth. The corruption of the artist by 'success' is the conventionally stated tragedy of the American artist.

8. His proper and fitting end is death in the service of the ideal—accompanied by the reward of bliss beyond
So Tristan and Isolde die in each other's arms—their love-death and transfiguration a matter of legend. Emma dies by self-administered poison, a pathetic offering on the altar of romantic love. Anna's suicide has an air of inevitability about it, and a quality that Tolstoy does not allow totally to redeem the sordidness of her later days with Vronsky (for both Flaubert and Tolstoy write as critics of the romantic myth). The true revolutionary heroes, like the true artists, are the dead ones—whose deaths permit us to reconstruct, retroactively, a romantic career for which death can be seen as the fitting end.

It is conventional wisdom that the value of the artist's work increases, Picasso to the contrary, after his death. His 'beyond' is posterity, which has taken the place of the bliss-in-after-life of the religious antecedents of courtly love.

The profile of the romantic lover is reflected in the profiles of the stereotyped revolutionary and artist. 'Fidelity', 'suffering', 'satisfaction' have different meanings in each case, but their relation to each other is in the manner of their relation to each other in the theory of romantic love. These correspondences, plus what is known of the development of the theory of romantic love and the emergence in the nineteenth century of the modern theories of artist and revolutionary, establish a presumption that these theories were founded on the projective model of the theory of romantic love. In the absence of a detailed analysis of the theories and of the historic continuity, however, the presumption remains merely an intriguing possibility.

Conclusions

CHAPTER VI

The Life of Metaphors in Theory: A Speculative Conclusion

The last chapter presented a series of illustrations of the conservative function of the displacement of concepts. In a number of cases we saw how the literal language of a theory gives clues about the older theories from which it has been displaced; how this displacement carries with it, often covertly and uncritically, assumptions drawn from the older theory; and how these, in turn, represent our tendency to retain as much as we can of our old ways of thinking, even as we adapt them metaphorically to new situations.

But these examples also suggest an evolution of theories. Our present views of the formation of new theories parallel early views of the origin of species: we tend to think in terms of denial of change or of 'spontaneous generation' (inspiration, strokes of genius), whereas the appearance and change of theories over time is much more suggestive of an evolutionary process. The displacement of concepts—the functioning of older theories as metaphors or projective models for new situations—is an essential process in this evolution, just as it is essential in the sequence of forms in a single process of invention.

This can be expressed in a simple line of argument.

There is novelty in the formation of concepts. New concepts are neither illusions nor law-like recombinations of old ones.

New concepts do not spring from nothing or from mysterious external sources. They come from old ones.

But how is this possible?

It is possible if new concepts emerge out of the interaction of old concepts and new situations, where the old concept is not simply re-applied unchanged to a new instance but is that *in terms* of which the new instance is seen. This is what we have described as the displacement of concepts—a process in which old concepts, in order to function as projective models for new situations, come themselves to be seen in new ways.

One way of looking at this kind of evolution is to think of metaphors as having lives of their own in the theories developed around them. Henri Focillon, in his *Life of Forms in Art*, conceives of certain basic forms—the ogive, for example—as organisms living in the environments of works of art. He sees them as changing in response to the demands of their environment; interacting with one another; passing through stages of emergence, vitality, and decay, in the manner of biological systems.

> It is my conviction that we are entirely justified in our assumption that such forms constitute an order of existence, and that this order has the motion and breath of life. Plastic forms are subjected to the principle of metamorphoses, by which they are perpetually renewed, as well as to the principle of styles, by which their relationship is, although by no means with any regularity of occurrence, first tested, then made fast, and finally disrupted (Focillon, 1948, pp. 5–6).

Metaphors can be treated in a similar way. There is here the possibility of a new kind of inquiry—an intellectual history which would consider not the manifest content of theories but the development of their underlying metaphors; a history of the displacement of theories; an account of the life of metaphors in theories analogous to the account, begun by Focillon, of the life of forms in art. It would attempt to describe the patterns of interaction and change in metaphor and theory.

The preceding chapter dealt with theories of deciding, theories of the mind, theories of understanding and of romantic love. Certain basic metaphors were discussed: the scale, the use of tools, social process, government, mechanism and dynamism, atomism, vision, the Christian life. Out of these considerations some general themes begin to emerge.

One of these is the notion that, in our culture, certain theories have had enormous durability. Operating metaphorically, protected by their covertness, the Greek theories of the scale, of atomic processes, and of vision, for example, have managed to preserve themselves virtually intact. We work now with theories of understanding based on the projective model of a theory of vision more primitive than Plato's. Some theories of ideas, current today, represent displacements of an atomic theory well known to Epicurus. Some contemporary theories of reason represent an aristocracy of the mind based projectively on a theory of society which may be found in the *Republic*.

As a corollary, in the light of the evolution of metaphors in theory, our intellectual space and our intellectual history seem greatly compressed. Theories drawn from many different parts of our intellectual world—theories of education, theories of business, theories of the mind, for example—appear to take their vitality, and their limiting assumptions, from a relatively small body of central metaphors: the metaphor of the machine and of the Christian life, to name two. Moreover, theories regarded as long dead—Solon's theory of justice, the atomism of Lucretius, the Christianity of eleventh-century Europe—function as vitally as ever as metaphors underlying the most contemporary theories. No one can look seriously at the life of metaphors in theories since Plato and fail to be impressed both by how *slight* a change there has been in the roots of our thought and by the unexpected homogeneity of our intellectual space.

Nevertheless, there has been evolution, and in the course of the narratives of the last chapter some of the more striking features of this evolution have suggested themselves.

One of these is the phenomenon of the dominant theory. The dominant theory seeks to spread itself over the entire span of the culture. We have discussed the theory of the scale, and its displacement to theories of legislation and rational decision. Atomic theories in the eighteenth and nineteenth centuries invaded, by displacement, theories of the mind, of society, of learning, perception, and thought. After the seventeenth century, however, both the scale and the atomic process fell under the domination of the Newtonian machine. Their histories can be seen as aspects of the engulfing tide of mechanism.

Directly as an instance of mechanical theory, mechanism encompassed chemistry—with the notion of chemical structures as mechanical assemblages of atoms (with chains, side chains, links, cross-links) and of chemical interaction as processes of mechanical collision, exchange, and replacement. In the work of Helmholtz and others, mechanism invaded physiology and neurology. What mechanism could not encompass directly it sought to engulf by displacement, and in this way it invaded not only theories of inanimate and animate things, but theories of the mind and of society as well. So we have 'trace' theories of memory, 'mechanisms' of perception, learning, and insight, 'machine' theories of business, 'mechanisms' of government, and the like. So deep is this penetration of mechanism and so unconscious has its metaphorical basis become, that in many areas of thought today rationality itself is seen to consist in nothing more nor less than the reduction of subject-matters to their appropriate mechanical bases. Inquiry has become a search for appropriate mechanisms, systems, devices, tools, and techniques. The basis of mechanism, in the use of man-made machines as projective models for the world, is reflected in the axiomatic view that, once we understand the 'mechanisms' of a process—whether it involves atoms, ideas, or people—we will be in a position to fashion tools to control it.

Medieval Christianity has exhibited a similar kind of dominance. Carl Becker, in his *Heavenly City of the 18th Century Philosophers*, describes the process by which the paraphernalia of Christianity—the notions of God, the after-life, salvation, sin, repentance—were (in our terms) displaced to form the theories of the eighteenth-century philosophers. The concept of an after-

194

life as a reward for right conduct, became the Utopian notion of progress—worldly happiness for posterity contingent on the rational efforts of present generations. Christian faith became faith in reason. Faith in reason, progress, posterity, went to form the theoretical building-blocks of our own society, still formally held, though seriously threatened by the events of the last two generations.

Christianity came to serve as projective model for the theory of the romantic lover and, through that displacement, for other critical roles in our culture. We all move in a sea of romanticism—which is, in effect, a sea of displaced Christianity. Tawney and others have shown how the forms and ideas of business can be traced to the Christianity—specifically, the Calvinism—of the Reformation. Early notions of salvation through works and of wealth as a sign of grace have been displaced, with loss of their explicitly religious content, to make up the formal values of present-day capitalism with its fervent moral defence of the acquisition of money.

The conflict of these dominant metaphors of mechanism and Christianity seems to underlie many of the uneasy social and artistic movements of our time. The notion of the self as machine is at odds with the notion of the self as romantic hero, whether lover, artist, or revolutionary. Since we are only peripherally aware of either identification, the conflict cannot be deliberately resolved. It expresses itself symbolically in our art, as in the machine-paintings of Duchamp. It comes to a head in our stereotype of the scientist, whose very role is full of commitment both to mechanism and to romanticism. It has confused our notion of war and of the hero: the romantic notion of the military hero is at odds with the notion of the soldier as military mechanic. It has undermined our traditional Calvinist morality: what are we to do with the idea of suffering as moral exercise, if suffering is also seen as the accidental breakdown of a mechanism which is in principle controllable? These and other perturbations of our time seem to me to be part of the coming together of two waves of displaced theory.

Conclusions

In these examples, we glimpse certain regularities in the life of metaphors: a 'law of maximum expansion' (metaphors will cover as much as they can) to complement a 'law of least change' (metaphors will change as little as they can).

Another theme of the life of metaphor has to do with certain persistent relations between metaphors and theories based on them. It is a truism to say that the culture provides us with the informal theories from which our formal theories are displaced. The culture provides the metaphorical gifts from which our theories are made. The theories we have been discussing would not have arisen if there were not in Western culture the balance scale, machines, the practice of medicine, a social structure involving an elite, and the like.

Moreover, there is some regularity in the relation between these theory-laden cultural entities and the formal theories to which they are displaced. Theories of the mind and of deciding, for example, seem to have been based on the metaphors of technology and of social structure. This seems to have been true of every intellectual era, from Plato's time to our own.

Technology and social structure have changed. Theories of the mind and of deciding have changed; but their change has been at a lag. Metaphors have a way of going underground in theories, so that notions of technology and of social structure long since 'dead' continue to be very much alive in theories of deciding and of the mind. The teleological machine—the machine full of parts interacting in lawlike ways so as to accomplish a preconceived end; typically, the watch—grew into the Newtonian machine which evolved into the dynamism of the late nineteenth century. But the model of the watch dominated Bishop Butler's thought. The Newtonian machine served as a projective model for theories of the mind—in mechanistic theories from Bentham to Pavlov to Watson—while Maxwell's theories were revolutionizing physics. And it is only in our own time that the metaphor of mechanism is being seriously and more or less effectively challenged in social and psychological thought, in such 'dynamic' theories as those of the Gestalt writers, Lewin, and Sullivan.

196

In an analogous way, machines of man's devising have provided projective models for his theories of the physical world and then, at a lag, for theories of the mind and of society as well. Engines, magnets, and devices for combustion had to be invented and more or less understood for the sun to be seen as an engine, the earth as a magnet, and the respiratory system as a machine for combustion. Theories of the brain and of the nervous system have tended to be based on the projective models of the most sophisticated and fashionable machines of the time.—Thus Descartes sees the nervous system as a hydraulic machine, Freud sees it in his 1895 project as essentially an electrical device, and contemporary cyberneticists treat it as a computer.

Darwin's idea of natural selection was a way of seeing in nature the projective model of man's age-old practice of selective breeding. Our technology and our institutions affect our thought not only directly, by the changes in behaviour they force upon us, but indirectly—by presenting themselves as projective models for our theories.

There are patterns of association among theories—some serving regularly as metaphors for others—and changes in the root theories are reflected only at a lag. The technology and the social structure of an earlier era are reflected in the formal theories of a later one. These formal theories become the basis of the common sense of a still later time. Changes in social structure and technologies may not be reflected in corresponding theories until many centuries have passed.

We have yet to see the directions of displacement which will be taken by quantum physics, the new biochemistry, the welfare state, automated industrial processes—in short, by all of the dominant theoretical, technological, and social innovations of our time.

The themes of the durability of metaphor and the compression of our intellectual time and space; of 'expansion' and 'least change' in metaphor; of conflicting patterns of displacement for theories in our culture; of the trend to association of theories in displacement—these are all aspects of a kind of history of ideas which would give to metaphor the role it deserves and has been denied (except for such writers as Cassirer and Jung). It would treat metaphor neither as an ornament of language (distinct from clear literal discourse) nor as a special kind of aesthetic meaning and truth (distinct from that of science and common sense) but as a process fundamental to innovation in theories of all kinds.

These themes of Chapter V force comparison with those of Chapter IV. There are parallels to be drawn between the development of theories in intellectual history and single processes of invention and discovery. The two can be regarded, in fact, as forms of a single underlying process, one an enormously expanded version of the other.

The historical displacement of concepts is always accomplished through processes of displacement carried out by individuals. Transposition and interpretation—the symbolic carrying-out of aspects of old theories and their placement as projective models in new situations—may go on over centuries. In Toulmin's example of 'light travelling', a process of displacement which appears to have begun with the Greeks, the notion of 'speed of the thing travelling' was in process of transposition from the seventeenth to the early twentieth century. Galileo and Michelson alike were concerned with it. In another area, several generations of economists have been engaged in carrying out the displacement of the Benthamite calculus (itself based on the metaphor of weighing) to the situation of economic choice. And, more recently, psychologists like Bruner have been displacing theories of economic choice to the process of concept formation itself.

But the parallel goes beyond the notion that historical processes of displacement are made up of partial processes of displacement carried out by individuals. It is also true that the two levels of displacement reflect one another. In both cases, old theory and old theory transposed to new situation may be said, after the fact, to be in a symbolic relation to one another. The relation between theories of the electromagnetic field and of the 'social field', as held for example by Lewin, are related to one another very much as are, in a single process of invention, the notion of a bus and of an 'air bus'. Moreover, the ongoing processes of transposition, interpretation, and correction are essentially similar in the two cases. In both cases, a law of least change—expressed in the inadvertent carrying-over of assumptions from the old theory—can be seen to operate. In both cases, central metaphors lead lives of their own in the process, underlying successive displacements which give them something of the character of theme and variations.

There would seem to be potential for inquiry in this notion of relatively brief processes of discovery and invention as microcosms for the development of theories in the history of thought. There is similar potential in the relation of the displacement of concepts to other processes—to behavioural learning, particularly child learning; to perception, especially the perceiving of one thing as another; to the historical development of technical innovation.

The central problem in all of these relationships, however, hinges on the process by which a familiar theory is brought as a projective model to a new situation, where new situation and old theory alike come to be seen differently so that one may be seen in the other. This process is at the heart of the displacement of concepts. It offers the hope of a non-mysterious treatment of the emergence of conceptual novelty since it permits us to explain the emergence of novelty as an interaction between two elements of the process, a kind of accommodation of these elements to one another. But what is the basis of this accommodation? What is the nature of the leverage the two elements exert on one another?

A consideration of the displacement of concepts, in its various forms, leads to these questions. And these questions lead in turn to an inquiry well beyond the present one.

BIBLIOGRAPHY

ARISTOTLE'S *Poetics* as in Richard McKeon (ed.), *The Basic Works of Aristotle*, London, Oxford University Press; New York, Random House, 1941.

BAILEY, CYRIL (ed.). Lucretius: *De Rerum Natura*, London, New York, Oxford University Press, 1947.

BENTHAM, JEREMY. *Principles of Morals and Legislation*, in E. A. Burtt (ed.), *The English Philosophers from Bacon to Mill*, New York, Modern Library, 1939.

BROWN, ROGER. *Words and Things*, Glencoe, Illinois, Free Press, 1958.

BRYANT, SARAH CONE. *Epaminondas and His Auntie*, Boston, Houghton Mifflin, 1938.

BURTT, EDWIN A. (ed.). *The English Philosophers from Bacon to Mill*, New York, Modern Library, 1939.

BUTLER, JOSEPH. *Sermons*, in A. I. Melden (ed.), *Ethical Theories*, Englewood Cliffs, Prentice-Hall, (2nd ed.) 1955.

CASSIRER, ERNST. *Language and Myth*, New York, Dover, 1946.

DAMPIER, WILLIAM CECIL. *Shorter History of Science*, New York, Macmillan, 1944.

DE ROUGEMONT, DENIS. *Passion and Society*, London, Faber; under the title *Love in the Western World*, New York, Pantheon, 1956.

DESCARTES, RENÉ. *Descartes Selections*, (ed.) Ralph M. Eaton, New York, Charles Scribner's Sons, 1927.

DEWEY, JOHN. *Logic: Theory of Inquiry*, New York, H. Holt and Co, 1938.

EATON, RALPH M. (ed.). *Descartes Selections*, New York, Charles Scribner's Sons, 1927.

EINSTEIN, ALBERT, and INFELD, LEOPOLD. *The Evolution of Physics*, New York, Simon and Schuster, 1938.

FOCILLON, HENRI. *Life of Forms in Art*, New York, Wittenborn, Shultz, 1948.

FROMM, ERICH. *The Forgotten Language*, New York, Rinehart, 1951.

GHISELIN, BREWSTER (ed.). *The Creative Process*, Berkeley, University of California Press; Mentor Books ed., 1955.

GILFILLAN, S. COLUM. *The Sociology of Invention*, Chicago, Follett, 1935.

HANSON, NORWOOD RUSSELL. *Patterns of Discovery*, London, New York, Cambridge University Press, 1958.

HOBBES, THOMAS. *Leviathan*, in E. A. Burtt (ed.), *The English Philosophers from Bacon to Mill*, New York, Modern Library, 1939.

HOFFDING, HARALD. *Le Concept d'analogie*, Paris, J. Vrin, 1931.

HUME, DAVID. *Enquiry Concerning Human Understanding*, in E. A. Burtt (ed.), *The English Philosophers from Bacon to Mill*, New York, Modern Library, 1939.

HUME, DAVID. *Enquiry Concerning the Principles of Morals*, in A. I. Melden (ed.), *Ethical Theories*, Englewood Cliffs, Prentice-Hall, (2nd ed.) 1955.

JAEGER, WERNER. *Paideia: The Ideals of Greek Culture*, London, New York, Oxford University Press, 1945.

KANT, IMMANUEL. *Foundations of the Metaphysics of Morals*, in A. I. Melden (ed.), *Ethical Theories*, Englewood Cliffs, Prentice-Hall, (2nd ed.) 1955.

KÖHLER, WOLFGANG. *Gestalt Psychology*, New York, Liveright, 1947.

KÖHLER, WOLFGANG. *The Mentality of Apes*, New York, Humanities Press, 1948.

LANGER, SUSANNE K. *Philosophy in a New Key*, Cambridge, Mass., Harvard University Press, 1957.

LEIRIS, MICHEL. *A Suite of 180 Drawings by Picasso*, New York, Modern Library, 1954.

LEWIN, KURT. *Dynamic Theory of Personality*, New York, McGraw-Hill, 1935.

LEWIS, C. I. *An Analysis of Knowledge and Valuation*, Lasalle, Illinois, Open Court, 1946.

LEWIS, C. S. *The Allegory of Love*, Oxford, The Clarendon Press, 1958.

LOCKE, JOHN. *Concerning Human Understanding*, in E. A. Burtt (ed.), *The English Philosophers from Bacon to Mill*, New York, Modern Library, 1939.

LUCRETIUS. *De Rerum Natura*, (ed.) Cyril Bailey, London, New York, Oxford University Press, 1947.

MCKEON, RICHARD (ed.). *The Basic Works of Aristotle*, London, Oxford University Press; New York, Random House, 1941.

Bibliography

MEAD, GEORGE HERBERT. *Mind, Self and Society*, (ed.) Charles W. Morriss, Chicago, University of Chicago Press, 1934.

MELDEN, A. I. (ed.). *Ethical Theories*, Englewood Cliffs, Prentice-Hall, (2nd ed.) 1955.

OPPENHEIMER, ROBERT. 'Analogy in Science', *American Psychologist*, vol. 11, no. 3, pp. 127–135, 1956.

PEIRCE, CHARLES SANDERS, *Collected Papers*, 'The Justification of Belief', (ed.) C. Hartshorne and P. Weiss, Cambridge, Belknap Press of Harvard, 1960.

PLATO. *The Republic*, (ed.) C. M. Baker, New York, Charles Scribner's Sons, 1927.

POINCARÉ, HENRI. *The Foundation of Science* (Chapter on 'Mathematical Creation'), in Brewster Ghiselin (ed.), *The Creative Process*, New York, Mentor, 1955.

POLYA, G. *How to Solve it*, Princeton, Princeton University Press, 1945.

POPPER, KARL. *The Logic of Discovery*, New York, Basic Books, 1959.

ROVERE, RICHARD, *The New Yorker*.

STEVENSON, CHARLES. *Ethics and Language*, New Haven, Yale University Press, 1944.

SULLIVAN, HARRY STACK. *Clinical Studies in Psychiatry*, New York, Norton, 1956.

TAYLOR, PAMELA. *Selections from the Notebooks of Leonardo da Vinci*, New York, Mentor, 1950.

TOULMIN, STEPHEN. *The Philosophy of Science*, London, Hutchinson; New York, Harper, 1960.

VEBLEN, THORSTEIN. *The Theory of the Business Enterprise*, New York, Charles Scribner's Sons, 1923.

WALLAS, GRAHAM. *The Art of Thought*, New York, Harcourt, Brace, 1926.

WERTHEIMER, MAX. *Productive Thinking*, New York, Harper, 1945. Revised ed. New York, Harper, 1959; London, Tavistock Publications, 1961.

WILD, JOHN (ed.). *Spinoza Selections*, New York, Charles Scribner's Sons, 1930.

WITTGENSTEIN, LUDWIG. *Philosophical Investigations*, tr. by G. E. M. Auscombe, New York, Macmillan, 1953.

WOLFSON, HARRY. *Philosophy of Spinoza*, New York, Meridian, 1958.

INDEX

Index